REVISE 11+

Also available to support
English 11+ revision:

English Practice Book 1

English Practice Book 2

English Ten-Minute Tests

English
Assessment Book

Series Consultant: Harry Smith
Author: David Grant

THE REVISE 11⁺ SERIES

For the full range of Pearson Revise 11+ titles visit:
www.pearsonschools.co.uk/revise11plus

Pearson

Contents

		Page	Total marks
✓	How to use this book	1	
✓	Assessment paper 1	2	/54
✓	Assessment paper 2	12	/66
✓	Assessment paper 3	22	/64
✓	Assessment paper 4	32	/66
✓	Assessment paper 5	42	/59
✓	Assessment paper 6	52	/62
✓	Composition	62	
✓	Notes	63	
✓	Answers	70	

How to use this book

You will get the most out of these assessments if you approach them like real 11+ exams. This means you should:

- wait until you have covered all the topics at least once
- find a quiet room or a place where you won't be disturbed
- work through a whole assessment from start to finish
- time yourself, and make a note of how much you can complete in the allowed time
- mark your assessments and keep track of your scores.

If you struggle with one of the assessments or are not happy with your score, use these books to brush up your skills:

Practice Book 1 will help you get used to 11+ style English question types with lots of guidance and support.

Practice Book 2 will continue to develop your skills and guide you through even more challenging questions.

The **Ten-Minute Tests** cover all the question types in the Practice Books and let you practise your skills in ten-minute bursts.

Before the exam

- Make sure you know when and where your exam is taking place, and make sure whoever is taking you to the exam knows too!
- Get a good night's sleep.
- Eat breakfast or lunch as you will find it hard to concentrate if you are hungry.
- Make sure you have got blue and black pens, and a couple of sharp pencils.
- Bring a pencil sharpener and an eraser.
- Use the bathroom before the exam.

During the exam

- Read all the instructions carefully.
- Keep an eye on the clock so you know how long you have left.
- If you can't answer a question, move on to the next one.

After the exam

- Try not to worry about your results. You have worked hard and have already done all you can.
- You deserve a break! Do something you enjoy to distract yourself and unwind.

Remember: 11+ exams come in many different formats, so make sure you read the instructions very carefully. Some exams will ask you to write your answers, others may ask you to shade in the correct answer option. Find out as much as you can about your exam beforehand so that you are prepared.

Assessment paper 1

Instructions

Before you start

Make sure you have:

- a blue or black pen, or a sharp, dark pencil
- a clock or watch to time yourself.

Questions and answers

This test contains **one extract** and **43 questions**.

- Questions 1–15 test **comprehension**.
- Questions 16–43 test **spelling, punctuation and grammar**.

Some questions are multiple choice and some require a written answer.

Read every question carefully to make sure that you answer in the correct way.

Write your answers directly onto the paper.

Time

You have **50 minutes** to answer the questions in this test.

Work carefully and quickly. If you have time left at the end, you should check your answers.

If you do not finish in time, make a note of where you got up to and carry on. This is still valuable practice. When you mark the test, only count up the marks for the section you completed within the time limit.

Marks

The number in the box at the side of the page tells you the maximum marks available for each question.

There are **54** marks in total available for this test.

Comprehension

This text is from a short story by Arthur Conan Doyle called 'The Adventure of The Speckled Band'. In this section, a young woman has come to see the famous detective Sherlock Holmes and his friend, Doctor Watson.

'Good-morning, madam,' said Holmes cheerily. 'My name is Sherlock Holmes. This is my intimate friend and associate, Dr. Watson, before whom you can speak as freely as before myself. Ha! I am glad to see that Mrs. Hudson has had the good sense to light the fire. Pray draw up to it, and I shall order you a cup of hot coffee, for I observe that you are shivering.'

'It is not cold which makes me shiver,' said the woman in a low voice, changing her seat as requested.

'What, then?'

'It is fear, Mr. Holmes. It is terror.' She raised her veil as she spoke, and we could see that she was indeed in a pitiable state of agitation, her face all drawn and grey, with restless frightened eyes, like those of some hunted animal. Her features and figure were those of a woman of thirty, but her hair was shot with premature grey, and her expression was weary and haggard. Sherlock Holmes ran her over with one of his quick, all-comprehensive glances.

'You must not fear,' said he soothingly, bending forward and patting her forearm. 'We shall soon set matters right, I have no doubt. You have come in by train this morning, I see.'

'You know me, then?'

'No, but I observe the second half of a return ticket in the palm of your left glove. You must have started early, and yet you had a good drive in a dog-cart, along heavy roads, before you reached the station.'

The lady gave a violent start and stared in bewilderment at my companion.

'There is no mystery, my dear madam,' said he, smiling. 'The left arm of your jacket is spattered with mud in no less than seven places. The marks are perfectly fresh. There is no vehicle save a dog-cart which throws up mud in that way, and then only when you sit on the left-hand side of the driver.'

abc A 'dog-cart' is a cart with two wheels, pulled by a horse.

1   Sherlock Holmes says: 'I am glad to see that Mrs. Hudson has had the good sense to light the fire. Pray draw up to it'.
What does the phrase 'pray draw up to it' mean here? Tick **one** box.

☐ Please stand closer to me.

☑ Please move your chair closer to the fire.

☐ Please draw a picture of the fire.

1 mark

2   Why does Sherlock Holmes order a cup of coffee for the woman? Tick **one** box.

☐ Because he thinks she is thirsty

☑ Because she is shivering

☐ Because Mrs Hudson has lit the fire

1 mark

3 Explain in your own words why the writer uses a new paragraph for the section beginning 'It is not cold…'.

The author starts a new paragraph because Sherlock Homles thinks she is cold but Mrs. Hundson says she is not cold but it is fear.

[1 mark]

4 What literary technique is used in the following sentence? Write your answer below.

'her face all drawn and grey, with restless frightened eyes, like those of some hunted animal.'

simile

[1 mark]

5 **a** Which description best describes the woman in the text? Tick **one** box.

☑ She is terrified.

☐ She is cold.

☑ She is muddy.

b How do you know this?   She is shivering

I know that she is muddy because Sherlock Homles says that she has seven spots of mud on her.

[2 marks]

6 Find and copy a phrase that suggests the woman's worries have changed her appearance.

"The lady gave a violent start and stared in bewilderment" ✗ with restless frightened eyes   her hair was shot with premature grey.

[1 mark]

7 Why does the writer give a detailed description of the woman's appearance? Write your answer below.

The writer gives a detailed description to show that Shelock Homles can spot these details.

[1 mark]

8 The narrator describes how 'Sherlock Holmes ran her over with one of his quick, all-comprehensive glances.' What does this suggest about Sherlock Holmes' skill as a detective?

This suggest that Sherlock Homles can pick up small details through quick glances.

[1 mark]

9   a   From your reading of the text, is the statement below true or false? Tick **one** box.

Sherlock Holmes treats the woman kindly and with sympathy.

☑ true ✓

☐ false

   b   Which words tell you this? Find and copy them.

'Good morning, madam,' said Homles cheerily, soothingly; patting her forearm **2 marks**

10   a   Is the woman surprised that Sherlock Holmes seems to know so much about her? Underline your answer.

~~yes~~ no ✓

   b   Which words tell you this? Find and copy them.

'You know me then?' a violent start; started in bewilderment. **2 marks**

11   Is the sentence below written in the active or passive voice? Write your answer below.

The left arm of your jacket is spattered with mud in no less than seven places.

_____ passive _____ **1 mark**

12   In your own words, write down everything that Sherlock Holmes notices about the woman's appearance. Use evidence from the text.

Sherlock says that he sees a return ticket in the second half of her glove, he also sees mud scattered in no less then seven places. **2 marks**

13   Which word in the **last paragraph** tells you that Sherlock Holmes enjoys explaining to the woman how he knows so much about her? Write your answer below.

_____ smiling _____ **1 mark**

14 What does the **last paragraph** make you think or feel about Sherlock Holmes? Write your answer below.

The last paragraph tells me that Sherlock Homles is a very observant person and can spot many details about a person.

2 marks

15 Which phrase best summarises what the text is about? Tick **one** box.

☑ Sherlock Holmes is a great detective.

☐ A woman with a worrying problem has come to see Sherlock Holmes.

☐ The woman is frightened.

1 mark

Spelling, punctuation and grammar

16 Underline **three** words in the sentence below that should begin with a capital letter.

<u>every</u> summer, <u>i</u> go to visit my aunt and uncle in <u>scotland</u>.

1 mark

17 Rewrite the sentence below using brackets to punctuate the parenthesis.

Nobody knows although many people think they know why human beings dream when they are asleep.

Nobody knows (although many people thinking they know) why human beings dream when they are asleep.

1 mark

18 Rewrite the sentence below using **two** contractions.

I had not realised that you could not swim.

I hadn't realised that you couldn't swim.

1 mark

19 Punctuate the sentence below with a semi-colon.

It was the last day of the summer holidays ; I was feeling miserable.

20 Which sentence is punctuated correctly? Tick **one** box.

☐ 'Whose turn is it to put the bins out' asked Dad.

☑ 'Whose turn is it to put the bins out?' asked Dad.

☐ 'Whose turn is it to put the bins out, asked Dad.

☐ 'Whose turn is it to put the bins out.' asked Dad.

21 Circle the correct spellings in brackets in the sentence below.

(Its' / (It's) / Its) a long time since our dog had (its' / it's / (its)) vaccinations.

22 In which section is the punctuation mistake? Circle **one** number.

Every night, my / sister tries (usually / successfully to avoid / doing the washing up.

  1   2   ③   4

23 Which sentence is punctuated correctly? Tick **one** box.

☐ Are you doing anything interesting in the summer holidays.

☐ I would like to go on holiday but it is very expensive?

☑ There are lots of interesting things to do at home.

☐ Give me some suggestions

24 In which section is the punctuation mistake? Circle **one** number.

'It's taking part / that matters' said / Ms Okafor, / 'not winning.'

  1   ②   3   ④

25 Which part of speech is underlined in the sentence below? Tick **one** box.

We hurried because they would be closing the <u>doors</u> in just a few minutes.

☐ adverb

☐ adjective

☑ noun

☐ verb

1 mark

26 Draw lines to identify the subject, verb and object in the sentence below.

The Normans invaded Britain in 1066.

subject   invaded

verb   The Normans

object   Britain

1 mark

27 Draw lines to match each sentence below with its correct tense.

My stomach is rumbling.   present perfect

It started to rumble two hours ago.   present progressive

I have not eaten anything since breakfast.   simple past

1 mark

28 Underline the preposition of place in the sentence below.

After an hour, we had to shelter <u>under</u> some trees until it had stopped raining.

1 mark

29 **a** Underline the conjunction in the sentence below.

Victoria was just eighteen <u>when</u> she became queen in 1837.

b What type of conjunction is it?

_____ Suboarbanatiy _____
confunction

2 marks

8

30 Which main clause completes the sentence below? Tick **one** box.

Whenever I go round to my friend's house, _____ .

☐ I have known her for six years.

☑ we always listen to music.

☐ because we get on so well with each other.

☐ she only lives around the corner.

1 mark

31 Circle the correct preposition to complete the well-known phrase below.

If _____ first you don't succeed, try, try again.

in   on   (at)   towards

1 mark

32 Underline the noun phrase in the sentence below.

The world's largest suspension bridge was completed in 1864.

1 mark

33 Complete the sentences below by underlining the correct verbs in brackets.

a I (go / have gone / went) to chess club every Tuesday this term.

b I (am getting / have got / will get) better if I practise.

c I (enter / will enter / have entered) a tournament when I am good enough.

3 marks

34 Add the prefix **mis-** or **dis-** to each of the words below to give it the **opposite** meaning.

___dis___agree   ___mis___understand   ___dis___appear   ___mis___ behave

1 mark

35 Which word is spelled correctly? Tick **one** box.

☐ grotesk

☐ groteskue

☐ grotesqe

☑ grotesque

1 mark

36 Which word is spelled correctly? Tick **one** box.

☐ rythm

☑ rythmn

☐ rhythm

1 mark

37 The word 'lie' is a homonym. It can mean 'to be in a horizontal position' Write a definition of another of its meanings.

It can also mean the opposite of truth,

1 mark

38 Read the definition below and complete the word.

A school subject in which you study the countries, sea, mountains and people of the

planet Earth: ge ography .

1 mark

39 In which section is the spelling mistake? Circle **one** number.

The tougest meat that I / have ever eaten is the lamb / chop that my dad burnt / on the barbecue.

①   2   3   4

1 mark

40 Circle the **incorrect** spelling in each of the sentences below.

a We broke the chocolate bar into two halfs and shared it.

b Exhaust fumes from all the lorrys on the road made it difficult to breathe.

2 marks

41 Complete the sentence below by filling in the missing silent letters.

As we clim_b_ed on and on, my legs started to feel num_b_ and I began to dou_b_t if we would ever reach the top.

1 mark

42 Complete the sentences below by circling the correct spellings in brackets.

a The chair was so (uncomfortable / uncomfortible) I had to move.

b That kitten is (adorable / adorible).

c The main course was (horrable / horrible) but the pudding was nice.

3 marks

43 Which sentence is spelled correctly? Tick **one** box.

☐ It was quite embarassing when the magician made my watch dissapear.

☐ It was quite embarrasing when the magician made my watch dissappear.

☑ It was quite embarrassing when the magician made my watch disappear.

☐ It was quite emmbarrassing when the magician made my watch disapear.

1 mark

Total marks = 40 **/ 54**

[END OF PAPER 1]

Assessment paper 2

Instructions

Make sure you have:

- a blue or black pen, or a sharp, dark pencil
- a clock or watch to time yourself.

Questions and answers

This test contains **one extract** and **43 questions**.

- Questions 1–15 test **comprehension**.
- Questions 16–43 test **spelling, punctuation and grammar**.

Some questions are multiple choice and some require a written answer.

Read every question carefully to make sure that you answer in the correct way.

Write your answers directly onto the paper.

Time

You have **50 minutes** to answer the questions in this test.

Work carefully and quickly. If you have time left at the end, you should check your answers.

If you do not finish in time, make a note of where you got up to and carry on. This is still valuable practice. When you mark the test, only count the marks for the section you completed within the time limit.

Marks

The number in the box at the side of the page tells you the maximum marks available for each question.

There are **66** marks in total available for this test.

Comprehension

This text is from a website giving young people advice on how to stay safe online.

Be safe online

The internet is an extraordinary place. It's a huge platform on which you can communicate, discover, play, learn and laugh. However, just as a spider's web can catch flies, the worldwide web can catch people out, both adults and young people. The best way to avoid danger and stay safe online is to follow these simple, sensible rules:

- Don't put any of your personal information online. Never give out or post your address, phone number or email address. If you are asked to fill in personal information, leave the space blank. If anyone asks you for your address or phone number, tell a trusted adult at once. Your real friends will already know how to contact you!
- Think carefully before you post pictures online. Once you've pressed 'post', it's too late to take it back. Your pictures may be online forever, for anyone to see and share.
- Never say anything online that you would not say to someone's face. Talk to others in the same way that you would like them to talk to you – and don't forget that you are interacting with real people!
- You wouldn't talk to a stranger in the street, so be careful who you talk to online. Some people may not be who they appear to be. If you have any doubts, stop talking. And never arrange to meet up in person with anyone you have met online.
- If you see or read something that makes you feel uncomfortable or worried, walk away and talk to a parent, carer or teacher about your concerns.

Remember: the internet is a great place to learn and have fun. By following these few simple rules, you can stay safe and enjoy everything the online world has to offer.

1 Find and copy the word from the text that means the same as:

   a amazing   _____

   b talk.   _____

2 marks

2 a The writer uses the phrase 'spider's web' to refer to the internet. What literary device is this? Write your answer below.

   _____

   b Explain why this is an effective choice.

   _____

   _____

   _____

2 marks

3 Why does the writer think you should follow the rules suggested in the text? Tick **one** box.

☐ Because the internet is like a web

☐ Because they will help you avoid danger and stay safe online

☐ Because the internet is an extraordinary place

`1`
mark

4 What is the most important point in the **first paragraph** of the text? Tick **one** box.

☐ The internet connects people.

☐ The internet is a dangerous place.

☐ You can stay safe online by following some sensible guidelines.

`1`
mark

5 In your own words, explain why the writer thinks the rules in the text are needed. Use evidence from the text in your answer.

_____

_____

_____

`2`
marks

6 Are the statements below true or false? Circle your answers.

a The writer suggests you should be suspicious of anyone who asks for your personal information online.

true / false

b The writer suggests you should be polite and friendly when you talk with people online.

true / false

c The writer suggests you should talk to anyone and everyone when you are online.

true / false

`3`
marks

7 **a** Is it easy to remove pictures that you have posted on the internet? Circle the correct answer.

yes   no

b Which words in the text tell you this most clearly? Tick **one** box.

☐ 'think carefully before you post pictures online'

☐ 'it's too late to take it back'

☐ 'for anyone to see and share'

`2`
marks

8 Find and copy a phrase that tells you that people you meet online may not always be honest.

_____

1 mark

9 In which tense is most of the text written? Write your answer below.

_____

1 mark

10 Explain in your own words why the writer has used bullet points in the text.

_____

_____

1 mark

11 What type of text is this? Tick **one** box.

☐ fiction

☐ an advice text

☐ an article giving the writer's opinion

☐ an informative text

1 mark

12 a Is the style of this text formal or informal? Write your answer below.

_____

b Why do you think the text is it written in this style? Tick **one** box.

☐ It is written for adults and young people.

☐ It is a factual text.

☐ It is about an important subject.

☐ It is a humorous text.

2 marks

13 Why is the last paragraph an effective way for the writer to end this text? Tick **one** box.

☐ It reminds you to follow the rules.

☐ It highlights the advantages of following the rules.

☐ It reminds you that using the internet can cause problems.

☐ It highlights the advantages of using the internet.

1 mark

14 The writer describes the advice in the text as a 'few simple rules'. What impression does this create of the advice? Tick **one** box.

⬜ You should follow the advice because it is easy and straightforward.

⬜ It is obvious and you should know these rules already.

⬜ It is good advice so you should follow it.

⬜ There are a lot more rules the writer could have suggested.

1 mark

15 Write a short summary of the text.

_____

_____

_____

_____

2 marks

Spelling, punctuation and grammar

16 Rewrite the sentence below using the correct punctuation.

does anyone know where we're going asked Melissa

_____

_____

1 mark

17 Use the words below to write a sentence that includes a parenthesis in brackets. You can use additional words.

my teacher   Ms Webb   has a pet spider

_____

_____

1 mark

18 In which section is the punctuation mistake? Circle **one** number.

I love cabbage / and sprouts but / my Sister hates them / and will only eat peas.

1   2   3   4

1 mark

19 Punctuate the sentence below using a colon.

Remember this nothing is easy and everything worth doing takes time.

20 Punctuate the sentence below using a possessive apostrophe.

Nelsons ships defeated the Spanish and French navies at the Battle of Trafalgar.

1 mark

21 Rewrite the sentence below, using the correct punctuation.

i looked in the cupboard under the stairs and found a broken laptop a lot of dust and some dead spiders

_____

_____

1 mark

22 The text below has the correct punctuation but incorrect layout. Mark the places where a new paragraph should begin using a double slash (//).

'I've never been here before,' said Alice. 'I have,' said Romi, smiling. 'Twice,' she added. 'I've been three times,' said Sara.

1 mark

23 In which section is the punctuation mistake? Circle **one** number.

The car's engine was / rattling and its lights were flashing when / it stopped and / would'nt start again.

| 1 | 2 | 3 | 4 |

1 mark

24 Rewrite the sentence below using semi-colons to punctuate the list.

Leonardo da Vinci was an amazing man: he designed a tank (four hundred years before one was first actually used in the First World War) he made several important discoveries in the field of human anatomy and he painted the *Mona Lisa*, the most famous painting in the world.

_____

_____

_____

_____

1 mark

25 Which sentence contains a coordinating conjunction? Tick **one** box.

☐ I followed the recipe precisely but it tasted horrible.

☐ If I make it again, I think I will use a different recipe.

26 Underline **three** examples of the simple past tense in the sentences below.

When I was playing tennis in the park, I hit the ball out of the court. A dog caught the ball and ran off with it so now I will have to go to the shops and get another tennis ball.

27 Complete the sentences below by underlining the correct verb forms in brackets.

a Dolphins (is / are) mammals, not fish.

b Everyone I know (love / loves) dancing.

c My team (lose / loses) every single week.

28 Complete the sentence below using a noun phrase.

When we got to the supermarket, I asked if we could buy _____ .

29 a Which preposition completes the sentence below? Tick **one** box.

I looked _____ the window to see if it was raining.

☐ up

☐ through

☐ under

☐ above

b Which type of preposition is it? Tick **one** box.

☐ time

☐ place

☐ direction

☐ cause

30 Complete the sentence below using a subordinating conjunction.

I was amazed _____ .

1 mark

31 Write the name of the part of speech underlined in the phrase below.

It was an <u>incredibly difficult</u> test but I did my best.

_____

1 mark

32 Rewrite the sentence below in the present perfect tense.

My mum works in the garden while my dad cooks dinner.

_____

1 mark

33 Which sentence is in the passive voice? Tick **one** box.

☐ Alexander Fleming had an accident in 1928 and discovered penicillin.

☐ In 1928, Alexander Fleming discovered penicillin accidentally.

☐ Penicillin was accidentally discovered by Alexander Fleming in 1928.

☐ Accidentally, penicillin discovered Alexander Fleming in 1928.

1 mark

34 Underline the correct homophones in brackets in the sentences below.

a As they left the city, (they're / there / their) was a huge traffic jam to get onto the motorway.

b They took excellent care of (they're / there / their) garden over the summer.

c My parents rang and said that (they're / there / their) going to be late.

3 marks

35 Rewrite each root word, adding the suffix **-ing**.

a hope _____

b bake _____

c arrive _____

d agree _____

4 marks

19

36 Circle the correct spelling in each pair of words.

   a retreive / retrieve

   b diesel / deisel

2 marks

37 Complete the sentences below, using words that contain silent letters.

   a You must tie a _____ in the string to stop the conker falling off.

   b Does anybody _____ the answer to this question?

   c Somebody _____ on the door so I called, 'Come in!'

3 marks

38 Write the correct plural of each of the words below.

   a dish _____

   b fork _____

   c knife _____

3 marks

39 Add the prefix **un-** or **in-** to each of the words below to give it the **opposite** meaning.

_____bearable   _____active   _____noticed   _____sensitive

1 mark

40 Complete the sentence below by adding a suffix to the root word in brackets.

     In the end, I _____ that I had made a mistake. (admit)

1 mark

41 The word 'object' is a homonym. It can mean 'to oppose or disagree' ('Nobody objected when I suggested we should order a pizza.'). Write a definition of another of its meanings.

_____

1 mark

42 Complete each sentence using the correct plural of the word in brackets.

   a I have been saving up all my _____ to buy something nice. (penny)

   b I cleaned my _____ and went to bed. (tooth)

   c I was surprised to see lots of _____ on the farm. (goose)

3 marks

43 Which word rhymes with 'how'? Tick **one** box.

☐ cough

☐ enough

☐ bough

1
mark

Total marks = ☐ / 66

[END OF PAPER 2]

Assessment paper 3

Instructions

Before you start

Make sure you have:
- a blue or black pen, or a sharp, dark pencil
- a clock or watch to time yourself.

Questions and answers

This test contains **two extracts** and **43 questions**.
- Questions 1–15 test **comprehension**.
- Questions 16–43 test **spelling, punctuation and grammar**.

Some questions are multiple choice and some require a written answer.

Read every question carefully to make sure that you answer in the correct way.

Write your answers directly onto the paper.

Time

You have **50 minutes** to answer the questions in this test.

Work carefully and quickly. If you have time left at the end, you should check your answers.

If you do not finish in time, make a note of where you got up to and carry on. This is still valuable practice. When you mark the test, only count up the marks for the section you completed within the time limit.

Marks

The number in the box at the side of the page tells you the maximum marks available for each question.

There are **64** marks in total available for this test.

Comprehension

This text is an extract from the poem 'A Birthday' by Christina Rossetti.

My heart is like a singing bird
Whose nest is in a water'd shoot;
My heart is like an apple-tree
Whose boughs are bent with thickset fruit;
My heart is like a rainbow shell
That paddles in a halcyon sea;
My heart is gladder than all these
Because my love is come to me.

abc 'A water'd shoot' means a well-watered tree. 'Halcyon' means idyllically happy and peaceful.

1   Which sentence best summarises the poem? Tick **one** box.

☐ It is the speaker's birthday.

☐ The speaker loves nature.

☐ The speaker's love has come to see her.

1 mark

2   Find and copy **one** example of alliteration in the poem.

_____

1 mark

3   **a** Complete the sentence below by circling the correct word in brackets.

The poet describes a tree that has many (branches / apples / leaves) on it.

b How do you know this? Write your answer below.

_____

2 marks

4   In your own words, explain how the speaker in the poem feels. Use evidence from the text.

_____

_____

_____

2 marks

5 **a** Find and copy an example of a simile in the poem.

_____

b Explain what the effect of this is.

_____

_____

$\boxed{2}$
marks

Extract

This text is an extract from an article about superstitions.

Have you ever been disturbed by the unforeseen appearance of a black cat? Or gone out of your way to avoid walking under a ladder? Do you feel nervous on Friday the 13th? You are not alone. Superstitions have lived with us for hundreds of years and, while we may think that the mighty power of science has crushed our belief in superstitions, they are still remembered by many and feared by some today, their origins lost and forgotten in the mists of time.

It is a common misconception that the fear of the number 13 originates in the Christian belief that 13 people ate with Jesus at the Last Supper before he was crucified. Yet there is evidence that the fear of this number – so widespread that it has been given the name triskaidekaphobia – was common in the centuries before Christianity. Both the Romans and the Vikings feared the number, believing it could bring bad luck or even death.

The phrase 'touch wood' is still commonly used when people talk about their plans or intentions: 'We'll be going on holiday in July, touch wood'. The possibility that our plans will go wrong is a constant worry, and always has been, which is why our ancestors called upon the spirits of trees to protect them from bad luck. Touching wood was seen as a way of gaining those spirits' protection. Although few people now believe that spirits inhabit our trees, lots of people clearly still believe in bad luck and will do anything to avoid it!

6 Find and copy a word in the text that means the same as:

a sudden and unexpected   _____

b misunderstanding.   _____

$\boxed{2}$
marks

7 What does the phrase 'we may think that the mighty power of science has crushed our belief in superstitions' suggest about the modern attitude to science?

_____

_____

$\boxed{1}$
mark

8 In your own words, explain how superstitions can affect people's thoughts and feelings. Use evidence from the text.

_____

_____

_____

9 **a** What literary technique is used in the words below?

'their origins lost and forgotten in the mists of time.'

_____

b Why is this an effective description? Tick **one** box.

☐ It suggests that we cannot see clearly into the past.

☐ It tells you that time moves slowly like mist.

☐ It suggests that you cannot trust what people say.

10 Why is the first paragraph an effective way for the writer to begin this text? Tick **one** box.

☐ It helps the reader understand that superstition is still a part of our lives today.

☐ It helps the reader understand that science is not a mighty power.

☐ It shows how long people have believed in superstitions.

☐ It describes lots of different superstitions.

11 Explain in your own words the meaning of the word 'triskaidekaphobia'.

_____

_____

12 Is the clause below written in the active or passive voice? Write your answer below.

'The possibility that our plans will go wrong is a constant worry.'

_____

13 a How many people still believe in tree spirits? Tick **one** box.

⬜ lots of people

⬜ some people

⬜ no one at all

b Which word tells your this? Find and copy it.

_____

2 marks

14 What is the most important point in the **final paragraph** of the text? Tick **one** box.

⬜ We still 'touch wood' for good luck.

⬜ Our ancestors believed that good spirits lived in trees.

⬜ We will do anything to avoid bad luck.

1 mark

15 The writer says, 'we clearly still believe in bad luck and will do anything to avoid it!'
Do you think he is right? Explain why.

_____

_____

_____

1 mark

Spelling, punctuation and grammar

16 Rewrite the sentence below using **two** contractions.

I do not know why she has asked to see me in her office.

_____

1 mark

17 Which sentence is punctuated correctly? Tick **one** box.

⬜ My sister wanted to watch a film

⬜ We played a game and went to bed?

⬜ How many times has this happened.

⬜ We wondered if Mum would say it was too late.

1 mark

18 Rewrite the sentence below, using brackets or commas to punctuate the parenthesis.

Elephants the largest land animals in the world cannot jump.

_____

_____

1 mark

19 Underline all the words in the text below that should begin with a capital letter.

'hurry up,' said my mum. 'you need to walk faster or we'll be late.'

'don't worry,' I replied. 'we've got plenty of time.'

1 mark

20 In which section is the punctuation mistake? Circle **one** number.

Is it possible to strum / the strings, get the fingering / right and read the music / all at the same time.

    1   2   3   4

1 mark

21 Circle the correct preposition to complete the well-known phrase below.

People who live _____ glass houses shouldn't throw stones.

in   beside   at   above

1 mark

22 Which line of text below is punctuated **incorrectly**? Tick **one** box.

☐ 'I have good news,' said Mr Williams. 'The class won first prize in the poetry competition.'

☐ 'What have we won' asked Jem.

☐ 'A certificate,' said Mr Williams proudly, holding it up so we could all see.

☐ 'I thought it might have been something exciting,' whispered Jem, 'like a holiday.'

1 mark

23 What are the words below all examples of?

diamond ring   gold earrings   silver bracelet   pearl necklace

j _____

1 mark

24 Rewrite the sentence below, adding a parenthesis that John Milton was blind.

John Milton had to dictate all eighty thousand words of his epic poem *Paradise Lost*.

_____

_____

1 mark

25 Complete the sentence below using a preposition of direction.

I jumped _____ the ditch, clearing it easily.

1 mark

26 Complete the sentence below using a subordinating conjunction.

Mozart became famous _____ he was still very young.

1 mark

27 Underline the modal verb in the sentence below.

People may not agree with everything you say but it is important to express your opinion.

1 mark

28 Underline the relative pronoun in each sentence below.

a We decided to get the kitten that I picked.

b The kitten, which is white and brown, has incredibly sharp teeth.

c Even my dad, who is allergic to cats, loves him.

3 marks

29 Complete the sentences below by underlining the correct verb in brackets.

a A famous writer (visits / visited / has visited) our school a few weeks ago.

b She (is showing / will show / showed) us how to make our stories more exciting.

c I hope she (will come / came / has come) back again soon.

3 marks

30 Why is the sentence below **incorrect**? Tick **one** box.

A life-size replica of a diplodocus skeleton, which is affectionately known as 'Dippy', have been displayed at the Natural History Museum in London since 1905.

☐ The passive voice is not used correctly.

☐ The subject and verb do not agree.

☐ The main clause and subordinate clause do not match.

☐ An incorrect relative pronoun is used.

> 1 mark

31 In which section is the punctuation mistake? Circle **one** number.

Its always a / good idea to apply / plenty of sun cream / when it's sunny.

    1   2   3   4

> 1 mark

32 Rewrite the sentence below in the present progressive tense.

Ellie tries to tidy her room but the dog gets in the way and makes her room even messier.

_____

_____

> 1 mark

33 Complete the sentence below using an adverb.

You must make sure _____ .

> 1 mark

34 Complete the sentences below by circling the correct spellings in brackets.

a Use a pair of sharp (scissors / schissors / scigssors) to cut the shapes out of the paper.

b (Which / Wich / Wrich) came first, the chicken or the egg?

c It's the thing I love most in the (hole / whole/ wholl) wide world.

> 3 marks

35 Complete the sentences below using these homophones.

sent   scent

a I _____ her a text but she did not reply.

b The police dog picked up a _____ and raced off into the woods.

2
marks

36 Which word is spelled correctly? Tick **one** box.

☐ acciddent

☐ acident

☐ accident

1
mark

37 In which section is the spelling mistake? Circle **one** number.

When we were younger, / my brother and I fort / all the time but now / we are good friends.

1   2   3   4

1
mark

38 Complete the sentences below by writing in the correct spellings in brackets.

a The security guard was the first person to _____ the jewels were missing.
(notiss / notice / notise)

b The _____ were called and they arrived in just a few minutes.
(police / polees / polise)

c The criminals were quickly brought to _____ . (justiss / justice / justise)

3
marks

39 Add the prefix **il-**, **im-** or **ir-** to each word to give it the **opposite** meaning.

_____mortal   _____regular   _____legible   _____perfect

1
mark

40 Which sentence is punctuated **incorrectly**? Tick **one** box.

☐ There are two choices: keep running or give up.

☐ I couldn't wait for our trip to the zoo – I'd been looking forward to it for weeks!

☐ The roller coaster was amazing: the log flume was even better.

☐ There was no one there; the whole place was empty.

1
mark

41 Complete each sentence below using a word that contains a silent letter.

a I would like to learn a _____ language such as German or Spanish.

b 'I know a secret,' she _____ quietly in my ear.

c I pursed my lips and _____ to call my dog but she ignored me completely.

42 The word 'suit' is a homonym. It can mean 'to make someone look good' ('That outfit really suits you'). Write a definition of another of its meanings.

_____

_____

43 Complete each sentence below by adding a suffix to the noun in brackets to make an adjective.

a His jokes were very _____ . (humour)

b It was a _____ occasion. (joy)

c She felt extremely _____ . (envy)

d I felt incredibly _____ . (nerve)

Total marks = ☐ **/ 64**

[END OF PAPER 3]

Assessment paper 4

Instructions

Make sure you have:
- a blue or black pen, or a sharp, dark pencil
- a clock or watch to time yourself.

Questions and answers

This test contains **one extract** and **43 questions**.
- Questions 1–15 test **comprehension**.
- Questions 16–43 test **spelling, punctuation and grammar**.

Some questions are multiple choice and some require a written answer.

Read every question carefully to make sure that you answer in the correct way.

Write your answers directly onto the paper.

Time

You have **50 minutes** to answer the questions in this test.

Work carefully and quickly. If you have time left at the end, you should check your answers.

If you do not finish in time, make a note of where you got up to and carry on. This is still valuable practice. When you mark the test, only count up the marks for the section you completed within the time limit.

Marks

The number in the box at the side of the page tells you the maximum marks available for each question.

There are **66** marks in total available for this test.

Comprehension

Extract

This text is an extract from the novel 'Wuthering Heights' by Emily Brontë. Mr Earnshaw has just returned from a trip to Liverpool. Along with presents for his children, he has bought home an abandoned boy he found on the streets. The story is told by the family's housekeeper, Nelly.

We crowded round, and over Miss Cathy's head I had a peep at a dirty, ragged, black-haired child; big enough both to walk and talk: indeed, its face looked older than Catherine's; yet when it was set on its feet, it only stared round, and repeated over and over again some gibberish that nobody could understand. I was frightened, and Mrs. Earnshaw was ready to fling it out of doors: she did fly up, asking how he could fashion to bring that brat into the house, when they had their own bairns to feed and fend for? What he meant to do with it, and whether he were mad? The master tried to explain the matter; but he was really half dead with fatigue, and all that I could make out, amongst her scolding, was a tale of his seeing it starving, and houseless, and as good as dumb, in the streets of Liverpool, where he picked it up and inquired for its owner. Not a soul knew to whom it belonged, he said; and his money and time being both limited, he thought it better to take it home with him at once, than run into vain expenses there: because he was determined he would not leave it as he found it. Well, the conclusion was, that my mistress grumbled herself calm; and Mr. Earnshaw told me to wash it, and give it clean things, and let it sleep with the children.

Hindley and Cathy contented themselves with looking and listening till peace was restored: then, both began searching their father's pockets for the presents he had promised them. The former was a boy of fourteen, but when he drew out what had been a fiddle, crushed to morsels in the great-coat, he blubbered aloud; and Cathy, when she learned the master had lost her whip in attending on the stranger, showed her humour by grinning and spitting at the stupid little thing; earning for her pains a sound blow from her father, to teach her cleaner manners. They entirely refused to have it in bed with them, or even in their room; and I had no more sense, so I put it on the landing of the stairs, hoping it might be gone on the morrow.

abc 'Bairns' is another word for children or babies.

1   Find and copy **two** adjectives that describe the appearance of the child that Mr Earnshaw has brought home.

    1   _____

    2   _____

1 mark

2   Are the statements below true or false? Circle the correct answers.

    a   Mrs Earnshaw feels sorry for the abandoned child.   true / false

    b   Hindley feels sorry for abandoned child.   true / false

    c   Cathy feels sorry for the abandoned child.   true / false

3 marks

3 Why is Mrs Earnshaw angry with her husband? Tick **one** box.

◯ Because the child he has brought home cannot talk properly

◯ Because her husband is so tired

◯ Because they already have their own children to feed and look after

[1 mark]

4 a Which statement best describes the narrator of the text? Tick **one** box.

◯ She is kind and thoughtful.

◯ She is short tempered.

◯ She is unsympathetic.

b How do you know this? Write your answer below.

_____

_____

[2 marks]

5 What does the phrase 'vain expenses' mean? Tick **one** box.

◯ Buying expensive presents

◯ Spending money unnecessarily and pointlessly

◯ Spending money to improve your appearance

◯ Giving money to charity

[1 mark]

6 In your own words, explain why Mr Earnshaw brought the child home with him. Use evidence from the text.

_____

_____

_____

[2 marks]

7 Why does the writer give a detailed description of Mr Earnshaw's thoughts and feelings when he found the child in Liverpool?

◯ It shows why he decided to bring the child home.

◯ It tells the reader what Liverpool was like at that time.

◯ It tells the reader that he was upset.

◯ It explains why Hindley's fiddle was broken.

[1 mark]

8 **a** What has happened to Hindley's fiddle? Tick **one** box.

☐ It has been lost.

☐ It has been stolen.

☐ It has been broken.

b Which words tell you this? Find and copy them.

_____

9 The writer describes how Hindley 'blubbered' when he saw his fiddle, even though he is 'a boy of fourteen'. Why is 'blubbered' an effective word to describe his reaction?

☐ It suggests he is behaving like a spoilt baby.

☐ It shows he is unhappy about the child his father has brought home.

☐ It shows he is happy to see his new fiddle.

☐ It suggests he is angry with his father.

10 Explain in your own words what sort of person you think Cathy is and why you think this.

_____

_____

11 **a** From your reading of the text, is the statement below true or false? Tick **one** box.

Mr Earnshaw is pleased with Cathy's reaction to the abandoned child he has brought home.

☐ true

☐ false

b Which words tell you this? Find and copy them.

_____

12 Explain in your own words what the final sentence in the text makes you think or feel about the characters, and why.

_____

_____

13 Which tense is most of the text written in? Write your answer below.

_____

1 mark

14 Which of these points should be included in a summary of the text? Tick **three** boxes.

☐ Mr Earnshaw has returned from Liverpool with an abandoned child.

☐ Mr Earnshaw is exhausted.

☐ No one can understand what the child says.

☐ Mrs Earnshaw and the family's housekeeper are unhappy about the child's arrival in their house.

☐ Mrs Earnshaw calms down after a while.

☐ Hindley and Cathy are upset because their presents are broken or lost.

☐ Hindley and Cathy are unkind to the child.

3 marks

15 Write a short summary of the text.

_____

_____

_____

3 marks

Spelling, punctuation and grammar

16 Rewrite the sentence below using the correct punctuation.

when I want your opinion he said I'll ask for it

_____

_____

1 mark

17 Complete the sentence below by circling the correct words in brackets.

(Its' / It's / Its) not surprising that the guinea pig would not eat (its' / it's / its) food.

1 mark

18 Rewrite the sentence below, using a dash to punctuate it.

The audience cheered and clapped and stamped their feet it was amazing.

_____

_____ [1] mark

19 In which section is the punctuation mistake? Circle the **one** number.

Every Sunday when / we go for a walk, / i ask my parents if we / can get a dog.

        1   2   3   4 [1] mark

20 Underline all the words in the text below that should begin with a capital letter.

'we've got just one chance,' said a woman behind us. 'we need to run.'

'where to?' asked Cerys. [1] mark

21 Rewrite the sentence below using the correct punctuation.

There are many strange breeds of shark, the hammerhead shark which, as the name suggests, has a head that looks like a hammer, the frilled shark, which has around 300 teeth, the spined pygmy shark which is tiny (just 28cm long!), and many that are even more surprising!

_____

_____

_____

_____ [2] marks

22 Rewrite the sentence below using a possessive apostrophe.

The car belonging to my cousins is parked next to ours.

_____ [1] mark

23 Rewrite the sentence below using brackets or commas to punctuate the parenthesis.

Snowdon which is the tallest mountain in Wales is 1085 metres high.

_____

_____ [1] mark

24 Complete the sentence below using the correct punctuation.

If I could have three different pets, I would choose _____

_____ [1] mark

25 Underline **two** examples of the present perfect tense in the sentence below.

It is strange that scientists have sent rockets to the moon, have eradicated lots of terrible diseases, and are inventing robots that can replace humans, but they cannot cure the common cold. [2] marks

26 Which part of speech is underlined in the sentence below? Tick **one** box.

A few minutes later, the bell rang and we hurried home.

☐ adverb

☐ adverbial phrase

☐ noun

☐ noun phrase [1] mark

27 Underline the subordinate clauses in the sentences below.

a The school will be closed if snow makes travel conditions dangerous.

b When it is safe to do so, the school will reopen.

c You will be contacted if the school is closed. [3] marks

28 Which coordinating conjunction completes the sentence below? Tick **one** box.

We were all exhausted _____ we turned around and went home.

☐ so

☐ or

☐ and

☐ but

29 Rewrite the sentences below using the passive voice.

a I did the washing up.

_____

b My sister vacuumed the carpet.

_____

2 marks

30 Complete the sentence below using verbs in the correct tense.

We _____ in a great hotel in Spain last year, so Mum and Dad

_____ that we _____ at the same place this year.

1 mark

31 Complete the sentence below using at least one modal verb.

Cakes and chocolate taste delicious, but _____

1 mark

_____ a healthy diet.

32 a Underline the conjunction in the sentence below.

The match will be called off if it rains.

b What type of conjunction is it?

_____

2 marks

33 a Which preposition completes the sentence below? Tick **one** box.

I wore my old clothes _____ painting the fence.

☐ by

☐ for

☐ beside

☐ above

b Which type of preposition is it? Tick **one** box.

☐ time

☐ place

☐ direction

☐ cause

2 marks

34 Complete the sentences below by circling the correct words in brackets.

a I (shood / shoud / should) have done my homework as soon as I came home.

b (Autumn / Autumb / Autulm) is my favourite season of the year.

c I painted my bedroom a (suttle / suthle / subtle) shade of green.

3 marks

35 Write an **ough** word that has the same meaning as 'zero'.

_____

1 mark

36 In which section is the spelling mistake? Circle **one** number.

In the boxes, I / found some dead flys / and loads of my / mum's old dresses.

  1   2   3   4

1 mark

37 Complete the sentences below using these homophones.

sight   site

a There is a huge, noisy building _____ across the road from our house.

b Mum left me looking after my little brother, telling me not to let him out of my _____ .

2 marks

38 Add a prefix to these words to give them the **opposite** meaning. Choose from **mis-**, **dis-**, **in-**, **im-**, **ir-** or **il-**.

_____patient   _____logical   _____competent   _____allow

1 mark

39 Read the definition below and complete the word with **ie** or **ei**.

An area of open land, often planted with grass or crops: f_____ .

1 mark

40 Circle the correct plural spelling below.

index / indexes / indexies

1 mark

41 In which section is the spelling mistake? Circle **one** number.

I stood perfectly still / and lisened very carefully / but all I could hear / was the wind in the trees.

1   2   3   4

1 mark

42 Write **two** sentences that include two different homonyms of the word 'fine'.

1 _____

_____

2 _____

_____

2 marks

43 In which section is the spelling mistake? Circle **one** number.

I usually / remember to say / 'please' and 'thank you' / but I do forget ocasionally.

1   2   3   4

1 mark

Total marks = ☐ / 66

[END OF PAPER 4]

Assessment paper 5

Instructions

Make sure you have:
- a blue or black pen; or a sharp, dark pencil
- a clock or watch to time yourself.

Questions and answers

This test contains **one extract** and **43 questions**.
- Questions 1–15 test **comprehension**.
- Questions 16–43 test **spelling, punctuation and grammar**.

Some questions are multiple choice and some require a written answer.

Read every question carefully to make sure that you answer in the correct way.

Write your answers directly onto the paper.

Time

You have **50 minutes** to answer the questions in this test.

Work carefully and quickly. If you have time left at the end, you should check your answers.

If you do not finish in time, make a note of where you got up to and carry on. This is still valuable practice. When you mark the test, only count up the marks for the section you completed within the time limit.

Marks

The number in the box at the side of the page tells you the maximum marks available for each question.

There are **59** marks available in total for this test.

Comprehension

Extract

This text is an article about the writer Charles Dickens.

Many people consider Charles Dickens to be the finest English novelist of all time. He was born in 1812 in Portsmouth. With eight children and little money, his parents moved frequently in the search of work and financial security. In 1815, the family moved to London, then to Kent (which Charles loved) and then in 1822, with their finances failing, back to London. The situation did not improve: in 1824, Charles' father was imprisoned in the Marshalsea debtors' prison for six months because he could not repay his debts.

At the age of twelve, Charles was sent to work in a factory to help the family survive. His job was to paste labels onto pots of 'blacking' – a kind of shoe polish. His father's imprisonment and the experience of long hours and repetitive work in the factory had a profound impact on Dickens: he worked tirelessly for the rest of his life and championed the poor in his writing.

By the end of 1824, the family's financial situation had improved, and Charles was sent to school. He learned shorthand and then found work as a parliamentary reporter. In 1833 he began contributing stories and essays to magazines, using the pen name of Boz. In 1836 his first novel, *The Pickwick Papers* was published and was an instant success. Dickens was a prolific writer and soon more novels followed: *Oliver Twist* in 1837, *Nicholas Nickleby* in 1838, *The Old Curiosity Shop* in 1840, and many more. His novels were published in serial form in magazines: each week or month, a new episode would appear. Dickens' aim was to end each episode on a cliffhanger, leaving his readers eagerly anticipating the next instalment, and encouraging them to buy the next edition of the magazine! His reading public were deeply affected by his stories. In one instalment of The *Old Curiosity Shop*, a child named Little Nell falls fatally ill. Dickens was inundated with letters, begging him to spare her life. Contemporary accounts report that, when her death followed in the next episode, readers were inconsolable.

Dickens died in 1870. In 37 years of writing, he had edited 3 magazines, written numerous essays, articles, novellas and short stories, and produced 15 novels, of which one, *The Mystery of Edwin Drood*, was left unfinished at his death.

1   What type of text is this? Tick **one** box.

☐ fiction ☐ an advice text

☐ an article giving the writer's opinion ☐ an informative text

1 mark

2   **a**   Why did Dickens' parents move frequently? Tick **one** box.

☐ They wanted to live in London.

☐ They had eight children.

☐ They needed more money.

b   Which words tell you this? Find and copy them.

_____

2 marks

3   In your own words, explain why Dickens' father was sent to prison. Use evidence from the text in your answer.

_____

_____

_____ **2** marks

4   The writer says that Dickens was sent to work in a factory to 'help the family survive.'
What impression does this create of Dickens' family? Tick **one** box.

☐   They were unhealthy.

☐   They were in a very difficult situation.

☐   They were a very big family.

☐   They were lazy.   **1** mark

5   In your own words, write down everything that you learn from the text about Dickens' job in a factory.
Use evidence from the text in your answer.

_____

_____

_____ **2** marks

6   Why does the writer give a detailed description of Dickens' job in a factory?

_____

_____ **1** mark

7   **a**   Complete the sentence below by circling the correct word or phrase in brackets.

His father's imprisonment and his job in a factory had (a little / some / a huge) effect on Dickens.

b   How do you know this? Writer your answer below.

_____ **2** marks

8 a From your reading of the text, is the statement below true or false? Tick **one** box.

Dickens' first novel was not very popular.

☐ true ☐ false

b Which words tells you this? Find and copy them.

_____

2
marks

9 What does the phrase 'eagerly anticipating' mean? Tick **one** box.

☐ Excitedly wondering about ☐ Really looking forward to

☐ Reading Dickens' older stories ☐ Painfully tired

1
mark

10 Why did Dickens end each episode of his stories with a cliffhanger? Tick **one** box.

☐ They were published in magazines.

☐ He wanted his readers to buy the next issue of the magazine.

☐ He did not know what would happen next.

1
mark

11 a Find and copy **one** phrase that describes the public's reaction when they read about Little Nell's illness.

_____

b Explain what this phrase tells you about the effect that Dickens' writing had on his readers.

_____

_____

2
marks

12 The writer describes Dickens' readers as 'inconsolable' when they learned that the character of Little Nell had died. What does 'inconsolable' mean?

☐ It shows how deeply upset they were.

☐ It shows they were angry that Dickens had let Little Nell die.

☐ It shows that Little Nell was unwell.

☐ It explains why they did not want to read Dickens' stories any more.

1
mark

13 Which sentence best explains why the last paragraph is an effective way for the writer to end this text? Tick **one** box.

☐ It tells you when Dickens died.

☐ It tells you about the novel Dickens did not finish.

☐ It ends with his death and sums up his achievements.

☐ It explains that Dickens wrote many different things in his life.

☐ 1 mark

14 What is the most important point in the **final paragraph** of the text? Tick **one** box.

☐ Dickens died in 1870.

☐ He wrote a huge number of stories, essays and articles.

☐ He did not complete his final novel.

☐ 1 mark

15 a From your reading of the text, which of these descriptions best describes Dickens? Tick **one** box.

☐ He was unlucky.

☐ He was hard working.

☐ He was successful.

b How do you know this? Write your answer below.

_____

☐ 2 marks

Spelling, punctuation and grammar

16 Rewrite the sentence below using **two** apostrophes.

The bike belonging to Uncle James was parked outside the house belonging to my parents.

_____

_____

☐ 1 mark

17 Which sentence is punctuated correctly? Tick **one** box.

☐ 'This doesn't make any sense at all!' she shrieked.

☐ 'This doesn't make any sense at all! she shrieked

☐ This doesn't make any sense at all' she shrieked.

☐ 'This doesn't make any sense at all' she shrieked.

1
mark

18 In which section is the punctuation mistake? Circle **one** number.

Antarctica which is / also known as the South / Pole) is the coldest / place on Earth.

1	2	3	4

1
mark

19 Rewrite the sentence below using dashes, brackets or commas to punctuate the parenthesis.

My grandad who is ninety-three years old loves going to the gym.

_____

_____

1
mark

20 Rewrite the sentences below, linking them together to form one complex sentence.

We missed the bus. We had to walk to school.

_____

_____

1
mark

21 Rewrite the sentence below using colons and semi-colons.

We all brought some food, Sam brought some jam sandwiches, which looked as though he had sat on them, Arif brought some crisps (salt and vinegar, and barbeque beef), and Mel brought a half empty bag of sweets and a pile of empty sweet wrappers.

_____

_____

_____

1
mark

22 Rewrite the information below in **one** sentence, adding commas where they are needed.

He hurried through the streets. He ran across the car park. He climbed into his car. He drove away.

_____

_____ 1 mark

23 In which section is the punctuation mistake? Circle **one** number.

'I'm going to count to ten,' / said Dad 'and you'd better / be cleaning your teeth / before I get to ten.'

| 1 | 2 | 3 | 4 |

1 mark

24 Which sentence is punctuated correctly? Tick **one** box.

☐ I bought some chocolate a magazine and a new pencil case.

☐ Do you prefer ice cream or chocolate pudding.

☐ Can you imagine what I looked like.

☐ None of us knew how to get home. 1 mark

25 Which part of speech is underlined in the sentence below? Tick **one** box.

'This is going to be <u>the best party ever!</u>' cried Tom, jumping up and down excitedly.

☐ adverb

☐ adverbial phrase

☐ noun

☐ noun phrase 1 mark

26 Complete the sentence below using a preposition of place.

When you count to one hundred, you should put your hands _____ your eyes so you cannot see where the others are hiding. 1 mark

27 Which relative clause completes the sentence below? Tick **one** box.

We performed a scene from Shakespeare's play *Macbeth*,

☐ which he wrote in 1606.

☐ who was the greatest playwright of all time.

☐ whose future is predicted by three witches.

☐ where he wrote it.

28 Which sentence is written in the present tense? Tick **one** box.

☐ I shall do my best to eat a healthy diet.

☐ I should eat more vegetables.

☐ I am going to try to eat more salad.

☐ I will stop eating crisps and sweets.

1 mark

29 Complete the sentence below using a fronted adverbial phrase.

_____ we had eaten every scrap of food on the table.

1 mark

30 Which sentence is punctuated correctly? Tick **one** box.

☐ I did'nt realise they were Jules book's.

☐ I didnt realise they were Jules's books.

☐ I didn't realise they were Jules's books.

☐ I didn't realise they were Jules books.

1 mark

31 Rewrite the sentence below using the present progressive tense.

I looked forward to Christmas because I hoped to get a new bike.

_____

_____

1 mark

32 a Which conjunction completes the sentence below? Tick **one** box.

_____ Australia is 32 times larger than the UK, its population is 3 times smaller.

☐ Until   ☐ Because   ☐ If   ☐ Although

b What type of conjunction is it? Write your answer below.

_____

2 marks

33 Complete this sentence using a preposition of cause.

I keep fit _____ .

1 mark

34 Complete the sentence below using an **ie** or **ei** word.

It is better to give than to _____ .

1 mark

35 Complete each sentence below by underlining the correct spelling in brackets.

a The dog was (enormous / enormus), with huge, sharp teeth.

b We had a (fabulous / fabulious) time at the theme park.

c The audience burst into (spontanious / spontaneous) applause.

3 marks

36 In which section is the spelling mistake? Circle **one** number.

The diving team went / down to the shipreck / hoping to find treasure, / but returned empty-handed.

1   2   3   4

1 mark

37 Complete the word below.

def___nite

1 mark

38 Which word rhymes with 'chew'? Tick **one** box.

☐ though   ☐ through   ☐ thought

1 mark

39 Write **two** sentences including the homophones below.

     wait   weight

1 _____

2 _____

|2|
marks

40 Find the incorrect spelling in each sentence. Write the correct spelling on the line below.

  a There were lots of other families with huge numbers of children in the restarant.

     _____

  b She escaped with no major injurys other than a couple of bruises and scratches.

     _____

|2|
marks

41 Circle the correct spelling below.

     carachter / character / caracter

|1|
mark

42 Read the definitions below and complete the words.

  a Where your mind stores information that you remember: m_____ .

  b A drug to prevent or treat illness: m_____ .

|2|
marks

43 Complete each sentence below by adding a suffix to the root words in brackets.

  a What could be more important than a good _____ ? (educate)

  b They wanted to know what she looked like and asked for a short _____ . (describe)

  c His face was filled with a look of complete _____ . (confuse)

  d He decided that this was the time to take _____ . (act)

|4|
marks

Total marks = ☐ **/ 59**

[END OF PAPER 5]

Assessment paper 6

Instructions

Before you start

Make sure you have:
- a blue or black pen, or a sharp, dark pencil
- a clock or watch to time yourself.

Questions and answers

This test contains **two extracts** and **43 questions**.
- Questions 1–15 test **comprehension**.
- Questions 16–43 test **spelling, punctuation and grammar**.

Some questions are multiple choice and some require a written answer.

Read every question carefully to make sure that you answer in the correct way.

Write your answers directly onto the paper.

Time

You have **50 minutes** to answer the questions in this test.

Work carefully and quickly. If you have time left at the end, you should check your answers.

If you do not finish in time, make a note of where you got up to and carry on. This is still valuable practice. When you mark the test, only count up the marks for the section you completed within the time limit.

Marks

The number in the box at the side of the page tells you the maximum marks available for each question.

There are **62** marks in total available for this test.

Comprehension

Extract

This is an extract from the play 'Macbeth' by William Shakespeare. In this section, three witches are preparing a magic spell.

First Witch

Round about the cauldron go;
In the poison'd entrails throw.
Toad, that under cold stone
Days and nights has thirty-one
Swelter'd venom sleeping got,
Boil thou first i' the charmed pot.

All

Double, double, toil and trouble;
Fire burn, and cauldron bubble.

Second Witch

Fillet of a fenny snake,
In the cauldron boil and bake;
Eye of newt and toe of frog,
Wool of bat and tongue of dog,
Adder's fork and blind-worm's sting,
Lizard's leg and howlet's wing,
For a charm of powerful trouble,
Like a hell-broth boil and bubble.

All

Double, double, toil and trouble;
Fire burn and cauldron bubble.

abc 'A 'fenny snake' is a snake that lives in marshy places.
A 'blind-worm' is a small but deadly snake.
A 'howlet' is an old-fashioned word for an owl.

---

1 Why is the mixture in the cauldron bubbling? Tick **one** box.

☐ Because there is a fire beneath the cauldron, making the mixture boil

☐ Because of all the different ingredients the witches have added to the mixture

☐ Because it is a magic spell

> **1**
> mark

2 a Are the witches making a spell to cause happiness or to cause harm? Tick **one** box.

☐ happiness ☐ harm

b Which words in the text tell you this? Tick **one** box.

☐ 'In the poison'd entrails throw'

☐ 'a charm of powerful trouble'

☐ 'Like a hell-broth boil and bubble'

> **2**
> marks

3 Find and copy the word in the text that means the same as:

a poison   _____

b magical.   _____

[2 marks]

4 Find and copy **two** examples of alliteration in the text.

1 _____

2 _____

[2 marks]

5 In your own words, explain what kind of people the witches are. Use evidence from the text in your answer.

_____

_____

_____

_____

[2 marks]

Extract

This text is an extract from the novel 'The Woman in White' by Wilkie Collins. In this section, Count Fosco meets a dog.

'Mind that dog, sir,' said the groom; 'he flies at everybody!'

'He does that, my friend,' replied the Count quietly, 'because everybody is afraid of him. Let us see if he flies at me.' And he laid his plump, yellow-white fingers upon the formidable brute's head, and looked him straight in the eyes. 'You big dogs are all cowards,' he said, addressing the animal contemptuously, with his face and the dog's within an inch of each other. 'You would kill a poor cat, you infernal coward. You would fly at a starving beggar, you infernal coward. Anything that you can surprise unawares – anything that is afraid of your big body, and your wicked white teeth, and your slobbering, bloodthirsty mouth, is the thing you like to fly at. You could throttle me at this moment, you mean, miserable bully, and you daren't so much as look me in the face, because I'm not afraid of you. Will you think better of it, and try your teeth in my fat neck? Bah! not you!' He turned away, laughing at the astonishment of the men in the yard, and the dog crept back meekly to his kennel. 'Ah! my nice waistcoat!' he said pathetically. 'I am sorry I came here. Some of that brute's slobber has got on my pretty clean waistcoat.'

> **abc** 'Flies at' is an old-fashioned phrase meaning 'to attack'.

---

6 **a** Complete the sentence below by circling the correct word or phrase in brackets.

     The groom is (afraid / not even slightly afraid) of the dog.

b How do you know this? Write your answer below.

_____

[2 marks]

7 **a** Complete the sentence below by circling the correct word or phrase in brackets.

Count Fosco is (afraid / not even slightly afraid) of the dog.

b How do you know this? Write your answer below.

_____

8 Find and copy a phrase that tells you how the dog usually behaves.

_____

1 mark

9 What does the phrase 'addressing him contemptuously' mean? Tick **one** box.

☐ Writing a letter quickly

☐ Patting his head quite roughly

☐ Treating him unpleasantly

☐ Talking to him disrespectfully

1 mark

10 **a** From your reading of the text, is the statement below true or false? Tick **one** box.

When the Count talks to the dog, the dog looks angrily at him.

☐ true

☐ false

b Which words tells you this? Find and copy them.

_____

2 marks

11 The count uses alliteration when he describes the dog as a 'mean, miserable bully'.
What is the effect of this?

☐ It gives emphasis to the Count's description, making him sound annoyed with the dog.

☐ It sounds good and suggests the Count is feeling happy.

☐ It makes it sound like the Count is reading a poem.

☐ It suggests that dog is frightened of the Count.

1 mark

12 The writer describes the dog as a 'brute'. Explain in your own words why this is an effective description.

_____

> 1 mark

13 a What effect does Count Fosco have on the dog's behaviour? Write your answer below.

_____

   b Which phrase tells you this? Find and copy it.

_____

> 2 marks

14 Explain in your own words what sort of person you think the Count is and why you think this.

_____

_____

> 1 mark

15 Write a short summary of the text.

_____

_____

_____

> 3 marks

Spelling, punctuation and grammar

16 Which line of text is punctuated **incorrectly**? Tick **one** box.

☐ 'Are we lost,' asked Mum, 'I'm sure we've been past that house three times now.'

☐ 'No!' laughed Dad. 'I know precisely where we are and where we're going.'

☐ 'I think we should stop and ask that lady for directions,' said Mum, sounding exasperated.

☐ 'I'm starving!' sighed my sister. 'Are we nearly there yet?'

> 1 mark

17 Rewrite the sentence below using **two** contractions.

    I could not understand why the television would not work.

_____

> 1 mark

18 Rewrite the sentence below, adding the parenthesis that Thomas was only six years old.

Thomas wanted to be an astronaut.

_____

_____

19 Which sentence is punctuated **incorrectly**? Tick **one** box.

☐ The river got higher and: it looked like it was going to overflow.

☐ She kept saying the same thing: 'I'm bored!'

☐ I love broccoli – it's delicious!

☐ I chose vanilla; Del chose strawberry.

1 mark

20 Which sentence is punctuated correctly? Tick **one** box.

☐ I would like a cold drink a toasted sandwich, and an apple.

☐ Please may I have pizza, garlic bread and a glass of lemonade.

☐ The waiter brought an enormous salad a jug of water and some bread and butter.

☐ I only ate one slice of pizza, some cucumber and none of the garlic bread.

1 mark

21 Which sentence is punctuated correctly? Tick **one** box.

☐ Sh'ed never believed she could beat Iris's record.

☐ She'd never believed she could beat Irises record.

☐ She'd never believed she could beat Iris's record.

☐ She'ad never believed she could beat Irises record.

1 mark

22 Rewrite the sentence below using the correct punctuation.

To keep safe on your bike always look where you are going, even if you're with an adult, be aware of other traffic around you, especially at junctions, and always wear a helmet.

_____

_____

_____ [1 mark]

23 Underline the subordinate clause in each sentence below.

a Although he is a famous historical figure, very little is known about him.

b He was greatly respected because he was so honest.

c When she finished, the audience gave her a standing ovation. [3 marks]

24 Complete the text below by underlining the correct homophones in brackets.

We took (to / two / too) cakes (to / two / too) Aunt Glenda and Uncle Barry's party. There was far (to / two / too) much food and we ended up bringing one home again. [1 mark]

25 Underline the **two** adjectival phrases in the sentence below.

Saturn is a much larger planet than Earth but it has a much shorter day. [1 mark]

26 Complete the sentences below using verbs in the correct tense.

Every week, I _____ to drama club. Soon, we _____

rehearsals for a show called *Oliver*. It _____ a musical about an orphan. [1 mark]

27 Which sentence contains a coordinating conjunction? Tick **one** box.

☐ She trained very hard but, sadly, did not win a medal.

☐ Her coach was pleased because she achieved her fastest time ever. [1 mark]

28 Rewrite the sentence below using the correct punctuation.

I have come to see you said the mysterious stranger because I have something to tell you.

_____

_____ [1] mark

29 a Which preposition completes the sentence below? Tick **one** box.

When we set off on our holiday, I had to get up _____ five o'clock in the morning.

☐ over ☐ in ☐ at ☐ on

b Which type of preposition is it? Tick **one** box.

☐ time ☐ place ☐ direction ☐ cause [2] marks

30 What part of speech is underlined in the sentence below? Write your answer below.

I pulled the sleeping bag up around my ears and settled down for <u>the longest, slowest, darkest night of my life.</u>

_____ [1] mark

31 Complete the sentence below using the correct conjunction.

if   although   when   because

I love my cat _____ I am not sure she loves me. [1] mark

32 Why is the sentence below **incorrect**? Tick **one** box.

A window was broke when we played football in the garden, which made Mum furious.

☐ The main clause and subordinate clause do not match.

☐ The subject and verb do not agree.

☐ The passive voice is not used correctly.

☐ The incorrect relative pronoun is used. [1] mark

33 Which sentence is written in the future perfect tense? Tick **one** box.

☐ This time next year I will be at my new school.

☐ Hopefully I will have passed the eleven plus exam.

☐ I think I will like my new school.

☐ I am going to work hard and make lots of new friends.

34 Circle the correct plural in each pair.

a ourselves / ourselfs

b replys / replies

c crashies / crashes

35 Rewrite the sentence below, using the correct punctuation

i played football on tuesday rugby on wednesday and basketball on friday so i was exhausted

_____

_____

36 Read the definition below and complete the word using **ie** or **ei**.

The daughter of a person's brother or sister: n_____ce.

37 Complete the sentences below by adding a prefix and a suffix to each underlined root word.

a The film was _____ <u>appoint</u> _____ because the story was so _____ <u>believ</u> _____ .

b My dog's behaviour is completely _____ <u>predict</u> _____ which makes him

_____ <u>poss</u> _____ to train.

38 Complete the sentences below using words that contain a silent letter.

a The _____ makes decisions about the way our country is run.

b Sometimes I use a pen to _____ and sometimes I use a pencil.

c The _____ on the door said 'Push'.

39 Complete the sentence below using the simple past tense of the verbs 'dust', 'mop', and 'scrub'.

I _____ , _____ and _____ until

the kitchen was spotlessly clean.

40 In which section is the spelling mistake? Circle the correct number.

We all thought it / was one of the most ridiculous / theories we had ever / heard in our lifes.

| 1 | 2 | 3 | 4 |

41 Write an **ough** word that is the simple past tense of the verb 'to bring'.

_____

42 Add a suffix to the adjective below to form an adverb.

final_____

43 Write **two** sentences each including a different homonym of the word 'space'.

1 _____

2 _____

Total marks = ☐ / 62

[END OF PAPER 6]

Writing

In some 11+ tests you will be asked to write a piece of fiction or non-fiction writing. This page provides you with a selection of questions that you can use to practise. You should spend about half an hour planning and writing each one. Use the notes pages provided, your own lined paper or an exercise book to write on.

Fiction

(30)

In your test, you may be asked to write a story.

- Write a story with the title 'Trapped!'

- Write a story with the title 'The Surprise'.

- Write a story about a journey into space.

- Complete this story.

  There was a ring on the doorbell. I hurried to the front door and threw it open. 'It's here!' I cried excitedly. 'It's finally here!'

- Complete this story.

  It was the strangest thing I had ever seen.

> A good story should include:
> ☐ a beginning that sets the scene
> ☐ a middle where an important event happens
> ☐ a satisfying ending
> ☐ accurate paragraphing
> ☐ a range of punctuation
> ☐ interesting word choices
> ☐ effective adjectives and adverbs.

Non-fiction

(30)

In your test, you may be asked to write a non-fiction text. This could be:
- an essay
- an article
- a letter
- a speech.

- Write an article about a sport or a hobby that you enjoy.

- Write an essay about a place that you would like to visit.

- Write a letter to your headteacher suggesting that the school should organise a student talent competition.

- Write a speech persuading people in your school to take part in a fancy-dress fun run for charity.

- Write an article with the title 'Keep your town tidy: stop dropping litter'.

> An effective non-fiction text should include:
> ☐ a clear introduction explaining what the topic is
> ☐ a middle with two or three main points
> ☐ a conclusion that summarises your ideas
> ☐ accurate paragraphing
> ☐ formal language
> ☐ conjunctions and adverbials to link your ideas and structure your writing
> ☐ a range of punctuation
> ☐ non-fiction features, for example a headline and subheadings in an article or a greeting (Dear…) and a sign off (Yours sincerely…) in a letter.

When you have finished writing, carefully read what you have written, using the relevant checklist above to check how successful your writing is. Tick each feature you have achieved, and note others as targets for future writing. You could also ask a friend or family member to read and check your writing.

Notes

Answers

The section links tell you which Practice Book (PB) to go to if you got the question wrong and want to revise the skill again.

Assessment paper 1

Pages 2–11

Comprehension

1 PB1 Section 8

Please move your chair closer to the fire.

> The word 'pray' means 'please' in this context, and the verb 'draw up' means 'to move closer'.

2 PB1 Section 8

Because she is shivering

> The explanation 'I observe that you are shivering' is linked to the previous clause, 'I shall order you a cup of hot coffee' by the conjunction 'for'.

3 PB2 Section 10

To show that the speaker has changed

> In a fiction text, look for a change in speaker, time and/or place when the writer starts a new paragraph.

4 PB1 Section 9

a simile

> The writer makes a comparison using 'like'.

5 PB1 Section 10

a She is terrified.

b Example: She is 'shivering' and says that 'it is fear' that makes her shiver.

> Any phrase from the text that suggests she is frightened is acceptable.

6 PB2 Section 12

Her hair was shot with premature grey

> 'Her expression was weary and haggard' would also be a suitable answer.

7 PB2 Section 11

Example: The writer wants the reader to understand how terrified the woman is and to feel sympathy for her.

> This is a 'why' question, so think about how this section of the text might make the reader think or feel. Alternative answers could be that it helps the reader to imagine the woman more effectively, or to show how scared she is.

8 PB1 Section 10

Example: It suggests that Sherlock Holmes is a very good detective because he is very observant and can understand a lot about a person through just a quick look.

> The word 'glance' implies a quick look, while 'all-comprehensive' suggests how thoroughly Holmes examines her.

9 PB2 Section 11

a true

b soothingly; patting her forearm

> Look for evidence in the text that agrees or disagrees with the statement in the question.

70

10 PB1 Section 12

a yes

b Examples: a violent start; stared in bewilderment

> These short phrases clearly suggest the woman's surprise.

11 PB2 Section 10

the passive voice

12 PB1 Section 12

Example: Her face is 'drawn and grey'; she has 'restless frightened eyes'; her hair is prematurely grey; she has a train ticket in her glove; her jacket is 'spattered with mud'.

> This answer includes all the important information in the text needed to answer the question, supported with evidence.

13 PB2 Section 13

smiling

14 PB2 Section 13

Example: Sherlock Holmes is very clever because he can tell a lot about the woman just by observing her. This suggests he is a great detective and will help solve the woman's problems.

> Remember to state your opinion clearly and explain it in detail.

15 PB1 Section 11

A woman with a worrying problem has come to see Sherlock Holmes.

> This summary focuses on the most important event in the text.

Spelling, punctuation and grammar

16 PB1 Section 3

<u>every</u> summer, <u>i</u> go to visit my aunt and uncle in <u>scotland</u>.

> A capital letter is always needed for 'I' and for proper nouns, such as the names of people or places.

17 PB2 Section 1

Nobody knows (although many people think they know) why human beings dream when they are asleep.

> Try reading the sentence with different parts left out. The part you can leave out without affecting the sense of the sentence is parenthesis.

18 PB2 Section 5

I hadn't realised that you couldn't swim.

> The apostrophes are positioned between **n** and **t** because **o** has been missed out.

19 PB2 Section 4

It was the last day of the summer holidays;
I was feeling miserable.

> Look for two different pieces of information that are of equal importance in the sentence, then use a semi-colon to separate them.

20 PB2 Section 6

'Whose turn is it to put the bins out?' asked Dad.

> Dad is asking a question, so there should be a question mark before the closing speech marks.

21 PB2 Section 5

(It's) a long time since our dog had (its) vaccinations.

> In each case, ask yourself: would 'it is' make sense here? Or is the sentence about something belonging to 'it'?

22 PB2 Section 1

3

> There should be a closing bracket after the word 'successfully'.

23 PB1 Section 3

There are lots of interesting things to do at home.

> The first sentence is a question. The second is a statement, not a question. The fourth is missing a full stop.

24 PB2 Section 6

2

> There should be a comma at the end of the first section of direct speech, before the closing speech marks.

25 PB1 Section 1

noun

26 PB1 Section 4

subject → The Normans

verb → invaded

object → Britain

> Remember: the subject does the verb to the object.

27 PB1 Section 2

My stomach is rumbling. → present progressive

It started to rumble two hours ago. → simple past

I have not eaten anything since breakfast. → present perfect

> The adverbials 'two hours ago' and 'since breakfast' give a clue to the correct tense.

28 PB2 Section 2   After an hour, we had to shelter <u>under</u> some trees until it had stopped raining.

> 'After' is a preposition of time. 'Under' is the only preposition of place in this sentence.

29 PB2 Section 3

a   Victoria was just eighteen <u>when</u> she became queen in 1837.

b   subordinating

> Subordinating conjunctions include 'when', 'because', 'although' and 'if'.

30 PB1 Section 4

we always listen to music.

> The subordinate clause begins with 'whenever', so this is the only option that makes sense.

31 PB2 Section 2

(at)

32 PB1 Section 1

<u>The world's largest suspension bridge</u> was completed in 1864.

> Make sure you underline all the elements that add information to the noun in the noun phrase.

33 PB1 Section 2

a I <u>have gone</u> to chess club every Tuesday this term.

b I <u>will get</u> better if I practise.

c I <u>will enter</u> a tournament when I am good enough.

> The adverbial 'every Tuesday' and the subordinate clauses 'if I practise' and 'when I am good enough' give a clue to the correct tense.

34 PB1 Section 5

disagree, **mis**understand, **dis**appear, **mis**behave

35 PB1 Section 6

grotesque

36 PB1 Section 7

rhythm

> Use the first letters of the words in this sentence to remember this tricky spelling: **r**hythm **h**elps **y**our **t**wo **h**ips **m**ove.

37 PB2 Section 7

Example: To say something that you know to be untrue

> For example, 'He said he would share it with me, but he lied'.

38 PB2 Section 8

geography

> Look carefully at the first three letters of the word and at the **ph** that makes the /f/ sound.

39 PB2 Section 9

①

> The correct spelling is 'toughest'.

40 PB1 Section 6

a ⬭halfs⬭

b ⬭lorrys⬭

> The word 'half' ends in **f**, so the plural is formed using -**ves** (halves).
> The word 'lorry' ends in **y**, so the plural is formed using -**ies** (lorries).

41 PB1 Section 7

As we clim**b**ed on and on, my legs started to feel num**b** and I began to dou**b**t if we would ever reach the top.

> All of these words contain a silent **b**.

42 PB1 Section 5

The chair was so ⬭uncomfortable⬭ I had to move.

That kitten is ⬭adorable⬭.

The main course was ⬭horrible⬭ but the pudding was nice.

> If the root word is complete, you usually add -**able**.

43 PB2 Section 8

It was quite embarrassing when the magician made my watch disappear.

> Notice the pattern of double and single letters in 'embarrass' and 'disappear'. Because 'embarrass' ends with a doubled letter, there is no need to double the final letter before adding a suffix.

Assessment paper 2

Pages 12–21

Comprehension

1 PB1 Section 8

    a extraordinary   **b** communicate

2 PB2 Section 13

    a metaphor

    b Example: It suggests how everyone is connected by the internet, comparing these connections to the many strands in a spider's web. The writer also uses the metaphor to suggest the possible dangers of the internet.

> Remember that a metaphor is a kind of comparison. Think about what qualities of a spider's web the writer wants the reader to think about in the text.

3 PB1 Section 8

Because they will help you avoid danger and stay safe online.

> Look in the text for key words and phrases from the question, such as 'follow' and 'rules'.

4 PB1 Section 11

You can stay safe online by following some sensible guidelines.

> All three points are included in the paragraph, but the first two are details supporting the third.

5 PB1 Section 12

Example: The writer thinks that the internet is like a 'spider's web' and can 'catch people out'.

> This answer includes all the important information and is supported with evidence. Other answers may be given (for example, people might not be who they say they are) but should be supported with evidence.

6 PB1 Section 10

    a (true)   **b** (true)   **c** (false)

7 PB1 Section 12

    a (no)   **b** 'it's too late to take it back'

> The first and third quotes help to explain why you should be careful when posting pictures online, but the second quote is the only option that highlights the difficulty of removing pictures.

8 PB2 Section 11

Some people may not be who they appear to be.

> Look in the text for key words or phrases from the question to help you locate the answer, such as 'some people' and 'not…honest'.

9 PB2 Section 10

present tense

> Look at the verbs in the text to help you work out the tense.

10 PB2 Section 10

> Bullet points are a common feature in information and advice texts.

Example: The bullet points highlight each piece of advice, organising the text and making it easier for the reader to follow.

11 PB2 Section 10

an advice text

> This text is factual. It gives the reader information and the writer's opinion, but the main aim is to give the reader advice.

12 PB2 Section 11

   a formal   **b** It is about an important subject.

A formal style can make the information or advice in a text more trustworthy and believable.

13 PB2 Section 11

It highlights the advantages of following the rules.

The final paragraph of a non-fiction text often summarises and highlights the text's key point.

14 PB2 Section 12

You should follow the advice because it is easy and straightforward.

The word 'rules' suggests you should follow the writer's advice. The words 'few' and 'simple' suggest it is easy and straightforward to do so.

15 PB1 Section 11 Example: You can stay safe online and enjoy using the internet by being careful with your personal information and pictures, being polite, being wary of strangers and talking to an adult if you feel uncomfortable.

The summary focuses on the advice given in the text and the reasons for following it.

Spelling, punctuation and grammar

16 PB2 Section 6

'Does anyone know where we're going?' asked Melissa.

Check carefully for speech marks and for closing punctuation at the end of the speech and the end of the sentence.

17 PB2 Section 1

Example: My teacher (whose name is Ms Webb) has a pet spider.

18 PB1 Section 3

(3)

'Sister' is not a proper noun, so it should not have a capital letter.

19 PB2 Section 4

Remember this**:** nothing is easy and everything worth doing takes time.

Colons are used to introduce lists, examples, quotations and explanations.

20 PB2 Section 5

Nelson**'**s ships defeated the Spanish and French navies at the Battle of Trafalgar.

The ships belong to Nelson, so an apostrophe and **s** are needed after his name.

21 PB1 Section 3

I looked in the cupboard under the stairs and found a broken laptop, a lot of dust and some dead spiders.

You need capital letter at the start of the sentence, a full stop at the end and commas between the items in the list (except for the last one).

22 PB2 Section 6

'I've never been here before,' said Alice. **//** 'I have,' said Romi, smiling. 'Twice,' she added. **//** 'I've been three times,' said Sara.

You don't need to start a new paragraph if the same speaker continues speaking. In this example, a new paragraph is not needed when Romi adds 'Twice'.

23 PB2 Section 5

(4)

The apostrophe in 'wouldn't' should be between the **n** and the **t** because the letter **o** has been missed out.

24 PB2 Section 4

Leonardo da Vinci was an amazing man: he designed a tank (four hundred years before one was first actually used in the First World War); he made several important discoveries in the field of human anatomy; and he painted the *Mona Lisa*, the most famous painting in the world.

> Count the number of items in the list, including their descriptions. Use a semi-colon to separate each one.

25 PB2 Section 3

I followed the recipe precisely but it tasted horrible.

> 'But' is a coordinating conjunction indicating contrast.

26 PB1 Section 2

When I was playing tennis in the park, I <u>hit</u> the ball out of the court. A dog <u>caught</u> the ball and <u>ran</u> off with it so now I will have to go to the shops and get another tennis ball.

> The simple past tense only uses a verb in the past tense. It does not need 'to have' or 'to be'.

27 PB1 Section 4

a   Dolphins **are** mammals, not fish.

b   Everyone I know **loves** dancing.

c   My team **loses** every single week.

> 'Team' and 'everyone' are singular nouns, so the verb must be in the singular form too.

28 PB1 Section 1

Example: When we got to the supermarket, I asked if we could buy **a delicious, crunchy, fresh salad**.

> A noun phrase is made up of a noun and any other words that add information about it.

29 PB2 Section 2

a   through   b   direction

> Read the sentence aloud with the different options and consider which one makes the most sense.

30 PB2 Section 3

Example: I was amazed **when I saw our new house**.

> Subordinating conjunctions include 'when', 'because', 'although' and 'if'. They link a subordinate clause to a main clause and can tell you:
> - where something happens
> - when something happens
> - why something happens.

31 PB1 Section 1

adjectival phrase

32 PB1 Section 2

My mum has worked in the garden while my dad has cooked dinner.

> The present perfect is formed using the verb 'to have' plus a past tense verb.

33 PB1 Section 4

Penicillin was accidentally discovered by Alexander Fleming in 1928.

> In the passive voice, the object of the action is the subject of the sentence.

34 PB2 Section 7

a As they left the city, <u>there</u> was a huge traffic jam to get onto the motorway.

b They took excellent care of <u>their</u> garden over the summer.

c My parents rang and said that <u>they're</u> going to be late.

> 'There' is used in a similar way to 'here' and has a similar spelling. 'Their' means 'belonging to them'. 'They're' is a contraction of 'they are'.

35 PB1 Section 5

a hoping   **b** baking   **c** arriving   **d** agreeing

> If the root word ends with a single **e**, you usually drop the **e** when you add a suffix that begins with a vowel.

36 PB2 Section 9

a retrieve   **b** diesel

> When the sound is /ee/, use **i** before **e** except after **c**.

37 PB1 Section 7

a You must tie a **knot** in the string to stop the conker falling off.

b Does anybody **know** the answer to this question?

c Somebody **knocked** on the door so I called, 'Come in!'

> All of these words contain a silent **k**.

38 PB1 Section 6

a dishes   **b** forks   **c** knives

> When forming the plural, add **-es** to words ending in **-sh**, **-ch**, **-s**, **-ss**, **-x** or **-z**. However, the word 'knife' ends in **fe** so the plural is formed using **-ves**.

39 PB1 Section 5

unbearable, **in**active, **un**noticed, **in**sensitive

40 PB2 Section 8

In the end, I **admitted** that I had made a mistake.

> Because 'admit' ends in a consonant-vowel-consonant pattern, and the final syllable is stressed, you double the final letter before you add the suffix.

41 PB2 Section 7

Example: A physical thing that can be seen and touched

42 PB1 Section 6

a I have been saving up all my **pennies** to buy something nice.

b I cleaned my **teeth** and went to bed.

c I was surprised to see lots of **geese** on the farm.

> Remember to add **-ies** to form the plural of a word ending in **-y**.

43 PB2 Section 9

bough

> The letter string **ough** is used to represent seven different sounds, for example: plough, trough, though, through, enough, brought, thorough.

Assessment paper 3

Pages 22–31

Comprehension

1 PB1 Section 11

The speaker's love has come to see her. •————————

> The third option is clearly stated at the end of the extract and is therefore the most effective summary.

2 PB1 Section 9

boughs are bent •————————————————————

> The /b/ sound is repeated in this phrase.

3 PB1 Section 10

a (apples)

b The poet describes 'the boughs… bent with thickset fruit'.

> The previous line tells the reader that the speaker in the poem is describing an apple tree.

4 PB1 Section 12

Example: She feels extremely happy, and is 'even gladder' than a 'singing bird', a tree laden with fruit, and a shell in the sea.

5 PB2 Section 13

a Example: My heart is like a singing bird

b Example: This is effective because the poet is trying to express how happy she feels and 'singing' is a sign of happiness.

> 'My heart is like an apple-tree' and 'My heart is like a rainbow shell' are also acceptable.

6 PB1 Section 8

a unforeseen   b misconception

7 PB1 Section 10

Example: That we believe science is very powerful, and that it shapes the way we think about things.

8 PB1 Section 12

Example: Superstitions can make us feel 'disturbed', 'nervous', or even make us want to go 'out of our way'.

> This answer summarises all the important points and supports them with evidence from the text.

9 PB2 Section 13

a metaphor

b It suggests that we cannot see clearly into the past.

> The writer compares the past to 'mists' but does not use 'like' or 'as', so this is a metaphor.

10 PB2 Section 11

It helps the reader understand that superstition is still a part of our lives today.

> This is a 'why' question, so think about how this section of the text might make the reader think or feel.

11 PB2 Section 10

The fear of the number thirteen

12 PB2 Section 10

active voice

Passive sentences usually contain the word 'by': 'The planet is being destroyed by pollution'.

13 PB2 Section 12

a some people **b** few

Look closely at the relevant part of the text, which is in the final paragraph.

14 PB1 Section 11

We will do anything to avoid bad luck.

The key point of a text or a paragraph is often found in the final sentence.

15 PB2 Section 12

Example: I agree with the writer because there is a lot of evidence in the text that shows how superstitions affect the way we think and act.

Remember to state your opinion then explain why you think that.

Spelling, punctuation and grammar

16 PB2 Section 5

I don't know why she's asked to see me in her office.

17 PB1 Section 3

We wondered if Mum would say it was too late.

The first sentence is missing a full stop. The second does not need a question mark because it is a statement. The third is a question, so needs a question mark.

18 PB2 Section 1

Elephants (the largest land animals in the world) cannot jump.
or Elephants, the largest land animals in the world, cannot jump.

Try reading the sentence with different parts left out. The part you can leave out without affecting the sense of the sentence is parenthesis.

19 PB2 Section 6

'hurry up,' said my mum. 'you need to walk faster or we'll be late.'
'don't worry,' I replied. 'we've got plenty of time.'

Look carefully for the beginnings and endings of sentences.

20 PB1 Section 3

(4)

This sentence is a question, so it needs a question mark at the end.

21 PB2 Section 2

(in)

22 PB2 Section 6

'What have we won' asked Jem.

Jem is asking a question, so there should be a question mark before the closing speech marks.

23 PB2 Section 8

jewellery

24 PB2 Section 1

Example: John Milton (who was blind) had to dictate all eighty thousand words of his epic poem *Paradise Lost*.

> Try positioning the additional information in different places to find where it makes the best sense.

25 PB2 Section 2

I jumped **over** the ditch, clearing it easily.

> Prepositions of direction include 'through', 'over', 'under' and 'past'. Choose the one that makes the most sense.

26 PB2 Section 3

Mozart became famous **when** he was still very young.

> The subordinating conjunction 'when' tells you the time something happens.

27 PB1 Section 1

People <u>may</u> not agree with everything you say but it is important to express your opinion.

> Examples of modal verbs include 'may', 'might', 'can', 'could', 'should' and 'must'.

28 PB1 Section 4

a We decided to get the kitten <u>that</u> I picked out.

b The kitten, <u>which</u> is white and brown, has incredibly sharp teeth.

c Even my dad, <u>who</u> is allergic to cats, loves him.

> Relative pronouns are words like 'where', 'which', 'who', 'that' and 'when'. They link a main clause with a relative clause.

29 PB1 Section 2

A famous writer <u>visited</u> our school a few weeks ago.

She <u>showed</u> us how to make our stories more exciting.

I hope she <u>will come</u> back again soon.

30 PB1 Section 4

The subject and verb do not agree.

> The verb 'have' should agree with the subject: 'A life-size replica... <u>has</u> been displayed...'

31 PB2 Section 5

(1)

> 'It's' is a contraction of 'it is'.

32 PB1 Section 2

Ellie is trying to tidy her room but the dog is getting in the way and making her room even messier.

> The present progressive tense uses a form of the verb 'to be' and a main verb ending in **-ing**.

33 PB1 Section 1

Example: You must make sure **you cook the chicken thoroughly.**

> Adverbs describe verbs. In this sentence, the adverb 'thoroughly' adds information to the verb 'cook'.

34 PB1 Section 7

a Use a pair of sharp (scissors) to cut the shapes out of the paper.

b (Which) came first, the chicken or the egg?

> Question words often begin with **wh**, for example, 'where', 'what', 'who' and 'whose'.

c It's the thing I love most in the (whole) wide world.

35 PB2 Section 7

a I **sent** her a text but she did not reply.

b The police dog picked up a **scent** and raced off into the woods.

> 'Sent' is the past tense of 'to send'. 'Scent' is a synonym for 'smell'.

36 PB2 Section 8 accident

37 PB2 Section 9

(2)

> The correct spelling is 'fought'.

38 PB1 Section 6

a The security guard was the first person to **notice** the jewels were missing.

b The **police** were called and they arrived in just a few minutes.

> Notice that all of these spellings end with **-ice**.

c The criminals were quickly brought to **justice**.

39 PB1 Section 5

immortal, **ir**regular, **il**legible, **im**perfect

> The prefix **il-** is usually only added to roots that begin with **l**. The prefix **ir-** is usually only added to roots that begin with **r**.

40 PB2 Section 4

The roller coaster was amazing: the log flume was even better.

> The second part of this sentence is a main clause, so it should be separated using a semi-colon.

41 PB1 Section 7

a I would like to learn a **foreign** language such as German or Spanish.

b 'I know a secret,' she **whispered** quietly in my ear.

c I pursed my lips and **whistled** to my dog but she ignored me completely.

> There are two silent letters in 'whistled': **h** and **t**.

42 PB2 Section 7

Example: A set of matching clothing, often a jacket and trousers

> A 'suit' is also the name for the sets in playing cards: spades, hearts, diamonds and clubs.

43 PB1 Section 5

a His jokes were very **humorous**.

> Notice how the root changes when the suffix **-ous** is added.

b It was a **joyous** occasion.

> 'Joyful' is also acceptable.

c She felt extremely **envious**.

d I felt incredibly **nervous**.

Assessment paper 4

Pages 32–41

Comprehension

1 PB2 Section 12

Example: dirty, ragged

> Adjectives are words that describe nouns. 'Black-haired', 'big' or 'older' are also acceptable.

2 PB1 Section 10

a (false)   **b** (false)   **c** (false)

> All of this information can be inferred from the character's words and actions.

3 PB1 Section 8

Because they already have their own children to feed and look after

> Mrs Earnshaw is angry because they already 'had their own bairns to feed and fend for'.

4 PB1 Section 10

a She is unsympathetic.

b Example: She refers to the child as 'it' throughout the text.

> Referring to the child as 'it' suggests that she thinks of him as an object or animal rather than a person.

5 PB2 Section 10

Spending money unnecessarily and pointlessly

> Look for clues in the context around word or phrase you are asked about. In this text, the phrase 'vain expenses' is preceded by a reference to 'money and time being both limited'.

6 PB1 Section 12

Example: The child was 'starving' and 'houseless' and nobody seemed to know 'to whom it belonged'. Mr Earnshaw was 'determined' that he would not leave the child 'as he found it'.

7 PB2 Section 11

It shows why he decided to bring the child home.

> This is a 'why' question, so think about how this section of the text might make the reader think or feel.

8 PB1 Section 8

a It has been broken.   **b** 'crushed to morsels'

> 'Morsels' means 'small pieces'.

9 PB2 Section 12

It suggests he is behaving like a spoilt baby.

> Think about what the writer's language choice suggests.

10 PB2 Section 12

Example: I think Cathy is unkind and spiteful because she spits at the child.

> Remember to state your opinion then explain why you think that.

11 PB2 Section 11

a false

b a sound blow… to teach her cleaner manners

> Look for evidence in the text that agrees or disagrees with the statement in the question.

12 PB2 Section 13

Example: I think the children are unkind because they refused to have the abandoned child in their room, and I think the narrator is unkind because she leaves him on the landing and hopes he might be gone the next day.

13 PB2 Section 10

simple past tense

> Look at the verbs in the text to help you work out the tense.

14 PB1 Section 11

Mr Earnshaw has returned from Liverpool with an abandoned child. Mrs Earnshaw and the family's housekeeper are unhappy about the child's arrival in their house. Hindley and Cathy are unkind to the child.

> Each of these points summarises a key idea from the text. The other points are all true, but are not as important.

15 PB1 Section 11

Example: Mr Earnshaw has returned from Liverpool with an abandoned child. This upsets his wife and their children, and they are unkind to the child.

> The summary focuses on the three key ideas in the text.

Spelling, punctuation and grammar

16 PB2 Section 6

'When I want your opinion,' he said, 'I'll ask for it.'

> Look out for sentences of direct speech that continue after phrases such as 'he said' or 'she said'.

17 PB2 Section 5

It's not surprising that the guinea pig would not eat its food.

> Remember, 'its' means 'belonging to it' and 'it's' is a contraction of 'it is'.

18 PB2 Section 4

The audience cheered and clapped and stamped their feet – it was amazing.

> Dashes are used to add extra information in informal writing.

19 PB1 Section 3

3

> The pronoun 'I' should always be a capital letter.

20 PB2 Section 6

'we've got just one chance,' said a woman behind us. 'we need to run.' 'where to?' asked Cerys.

> Look carefully for the beginnings and endings of sentences .

21 PB2 Section 4

There are many strange breeds of shark: the hammerhead shark which, as the name suggests, has a head that looks like a hammer; the frilled shark, which has around 300 teeth; the spined pygmy shark which is tiny (just 28cm long!); and many that are even more surprising!

> Use a colon to introduce a list. Count the number of items in the list, including any information used to describe them, and use a semi-colon to separate them.

22 PB2 Section 5

My cousins' car is parked next to ours.

> This sentence is about more than one cousin, so the apostrophe should come at the end of the word: 'My cousins' car...'

23 PB2 Section 1

Example: Snowdon, which is the tallest mountain in Wales, is 1085 metres high.

> Look for the extra information in the sentence.

24 PB1 Section 3

Example: If I could have three different pets, I would choose a dog, a cat and a hamster.

> Each item in a list should be separated by a comma, except for the last item, which is linked using 'and'.

25 PB1 Section 2

It is strange that scientists <u>have sent</u> rockets to the moon, <u>have eradicated</u> lots of terrible diseases, and are inventing robots that can replace humans, but they cannot cure the common cold.

> The present perfect is formed using the verb 'to have'.

26 PB1 Section 1

adverbial phrase

> An adverbial phrase is a group of words that give information about when, where or how a verb happens. In this sentence, the adverbial phrase tells you <u>when</u> the bell rang.

27 PB1 Section 4

a The school will be closed <u>if snow makes travel conditions dangerous</u>.

b <u>When it is safe to do so</u>, the school will reopen.

> Subordinate clauses can be positioned before or after the main clause.

c You will be contacted <u>if the school is closed</u>.

28 PB2 Section 3

so

> Read the sentence aloud with the different options and consider which one makes the most sense.

29 PB1 Section 4

a The washing up was done by me.

b The carpet was vacuumed by my sister.

> The subject and object swap places when a verb is put into the passive voice.

30 PB1 Section 2

Example: We **stayed** in a great hotel in Spain last year, so Mum and Dad **have decided** that we **will stay** at the same place this year.

> There are two or three ways to complete this sentence appropriately. Read your sentence aloud to make sure that it makes sense.

31 PB1 Section 1

Example: Cakes and chocolate taste delicious, but **you should try to eat** a healthy diet.

> Examples of modal verbs include 'may', 'might', 'can', 'could', 'should' and 'must'.

32 PB2 Section 3

a The match will be called off <u>if</u> it rains.

b subordinating

> Examples of subordinating conjunctions include 'when', 'because', 'although' and 'if'.

33 PB2 Section 2

    a   for   **b**   cause

> Prepositions of cause can indicate the reason for or the purpose of something.

34 PB1 Section 7

    a   I (should) have done my homework as soon as I came home.

    b   (Autumn) is my favourite season of the year.

> Remember, this spelling pattern is also used in 'would' and 'could'.

    c   I painted my bedroom a (subtle) shade of green.

35 PB2 Section 9

nought

36 PB1 Section 6

(2)

> 'Fly' ends in **y**, so the plural is formed using the suffix **-ies**.

37 PB2 Section 7

    a   There is a huge, noisy building **site** across the road from our house.

    b   Mum left me looking after my little brother, telling me not to let him out of my **sight**.

38 PB1 Section 5

impatient, **il**logical, **in**competent, **dis**allow

39 PB2 Section 9

field

40 PB1 Section 6

(indexes)

> 'Index' ends in **x**, so the plural is formed using the suffix **-es**.

41 PB1 Section 7

(2)

> There is a silent **t** in listen.

42 PB2 Section 7

Example: I had a headache yesterday but I feel fine today.
If you park on double yellow lines, you will have to pay a fine.

> 'Fine' can mean:
> - good or satisfactory (The weather was fine.)
> - agreement (That was fine by me.)
> - a sum of money paid as a penalty (I had to pay a £10 fine.)
> - thin or delicate (I sewed the button on with a very fine thread.)

43 PB2 Section 8

(4)

> The correct spelling is 'occasionally'.

Assessment paper 5

Pages 42–51

Comprehension

1 PB2 Section 10

an informative text

> Work through each option, rejecting them one by one until only the correct answer is left. This text is factual so it is not fiction. It doesn't give advice or an opinion. It does give the reader information.

2 PB1 Section 8

a They needed more money.

b in the search of work and financial security

3 PB1 Section 12

Example: Dickens' father was sent to prison because he 'could not repay his debts'.

> This answer includes all the important information from the text and is supported with evidence.

4 PB2 Section 12

They were in a very difficult situation.

> Look closely at the relevant part of the text about Dickens' job in the factory.

5 PB1 Section 12

Example: Dickens' job was in a blacking factory, pasting labels onto pots. It involved 'long hours and repetitive work'.

6 PB2 Section 11

Example: It helps the reader understand how desperate the family were for money, because Dickens had to do such a horrible job at such a young age.

> This is a 'why' question, so think about how this section of the text might make the reader think or feel.

7 PB1 Section 10

a His father's imprisonment and his job in a factory had (a huge) effect on Dickens.

b The text says it had 'a profound impact' on Dickens.

8 PB2 Section 11

a false   **b** instant success

> Look for evidence in the text that agrees or disagrees with the statement in the question.

9 PB2 Section 10

Really looking forward to

> Look for clues in the context around the word or phrase you are asked about. For example, this phrase is quickly followed by 'encouraging them to buy the next instalment…'.

10 PB1 Section 8

He wanted his readers to buy the next issue of the magazine.

11 PB2 Section 12

a begging him to spare her life

b The phrase suggests the public loved his writing because they cared so much about his characters' lives.

'Inundated with letters' is also acceptable.

12 PB2 Section 12

It shows how very deeply upset they were.

Look closely at the part of the text where the word is used.

13 PB2 Section 11

It ends with his death and sums up his achievements.

Biographical texts often end with information about the subject's death and a summary of their achievements.

14 PB1 Section 11

He wrote a huge number of stories, essays and articles.

The first the third points are mentioned in the paragraph, but the number of stories, essays and articles that Dickens wrote is the main focus.

15 PB1 Section 10

a He was hard working.

b Example: It says in the extract that Dickens 'worked tirelessly for the rest of his life'.

All of the points are expressed in the text, but references to his hard work and the amount of work he completed in his life are the most frequent.

Spelling, punctuation and grammar

16 PB2 Section 5

Uncle James's bike was parked outside my parents' house.

If a name ends in **s**, add an apostrophe and **s** to show possession. If a plural noun ends in **s**, just add an apostrophe to show possession.

17 PB2 Section 6

'This doesn't make any sense at all!' she shrieked.

Look closely at the punctuation at the end of the direct speech and at the end of the sentence.

18 PB2 Section 1

(1)

The opening bracket of the parenthesis is missing.

19 PB2 Section 1

Example: My grandad – who is ninety-three years old – loves going to the gym.

Look for the extra information in the sentence.

20 PB1 Section 4

Example: We had to walk to school because we missed the bus.

'Because we missed the bus, we had to walk to school.' is also acceptable.

21 PB2 Section 4

We all brought some food: Sam brought some jam sandwiches, which looked as though he had sat on them; Arif brought some crisps (salt and vinegar, and barbeque beef); and Mel brought a half empty bag of sweets and a pile of empty sweet wrappers.

Use a colon to introduce a list. Count the number of items in the list, including any information used to describe them, and use a semi-colon to separate each one.

22 PB1 Section 3

He hurried through the streets, ran across the car park, climbed into his car and drove away.

23 PB2 Section 6

(2) ——————————————————————— There should be a comma after 'said Dad'.

24 PB1 Section 3

None of us knew how to get home. ——— The first sentence is a list, so the items need to be separated by commas. The second sentence is a question, so it needs a question mark. The third sentence is a question, so it needs a question mark.

25 PB1 Section 1

noun phrase ——————————— A noun phrase is made up of a noun and any other words that add information it.

26 PB2 Section 2

When you count to one hundred, you should put your hands **over** your eyes so you cannot see where the others are hiding

27 PB1 Section 4

which he wrote in 1606. ——— None of the other options add information about the noun phrase 'Shakespeare's play *Macbeth*'.

28 PB1 Section 2

I should eat more vegetables.

29 PB1 Section 1

Example: After ten minutes, we had eaten every scrap of food on the table. ——— An adverbial phrase is a group of words that give information about when, where or how a verb happens. A fronted adverbial phrase is positioned at the beginning of a sentence.

30 PB2 Section 5

I didn't realise they were Jules's books.

31 PB1 Section 2

I am looking forward to Christmas because I am hoping to get a new bike. ——— The present progressive uses a form of the verb 'to be' and a main verb ending in -**ing**.

32 PB2 Section 3

a Although   **b** subordinating ——— Examples of subordinating conjunctions include 'when', 'because', 'although' and 'if'.

33 PB2 Section 2

Example: I keep fit **by walking instead of taking the bus**. ——— Common prepositions of cause include 'by', 'for' and 'due to'.

34 PB2 Section 9

It is better to give than to **receive**. ——— When the sound is /ee/, use **i** before **e** except after **c**.

35 PB1 Section 5

a   The dog was <u>enormous</u>, with huge, sharp teeth.

b   We had a <u>fabulous</u> time at the theme park.

c   The audience burst into <u>spontaneous</u> applause.

36 PB1 Section 7

(2) ——————————————————————————————— There is a silent **w** in 'shipwreck'.

37 PB2 Section 8

def**i**nite

38 PB2 Section 9

through

39 PB2 Section 7

Example: I had to wait hours for the bus. The weight of the box made it difficult to carry.

'Wait' is a verb meaning 'to stay where you are' or 'to delay an action'. 'Weight' is a noun meaning 'heaviness'.

40 PB1 Section 6

a   restaurant   **b**   injuries

'Injury' ends in a **y**, so the plural is formed using the suffix **-ies**.

41 PB1 Section 7

(character)

Notice the position of the silent **h**. This is the same **ch** pattern as in 'echo', 'ache' and 'school'.

42 PB2 Section 8

a   memory   **b**   medicine

43 PB1 Section 5

a   What could be more important than a good **education**?

b   They wanted to know what she looked like and asked for a short **description**.

Notice how the **b** in 'describe' becomes a **p** in 'description'.

c   His face was filled with a look of complete **confusion**.

d   He decided that this was the time to take **action**.

Assessment paper 6

Pages 52–61

Comprehension

1   PB1 Section 8

Because there is a fire beneath the cauldron, making the mixture boil

> The phrase 'fire burn and cauldron bubble' suggests that this is the correct answer.

2   PB1 Section 12

a harm   **b** 'a charm of powerful trouble'

> The first and third options both suggest an unpleasant spell, but the second option most clearly suggests the witches' aim to cause 'powerful trouble'.

3   PB1 Section 8

a venom   **b** charmed

4   PB1 Section 9

Example: toil and trouble, fillet of a fenny snake

> Alliteration is a sequence of two or more words close together that begin with the same sound. 'Boil and bake', 'lizard's leg' or 'boil and bubble' are also acceptable.

5   PB1 Section 12

Example: The witches are disturbing because they are using very strange ingredients such as 'eye of newt' and 'tongue of dog'. This makes you wonder how they will use the evil magic they are creating.

> This answer uses a range of evidence from the text to answer the question.

6   PB1 Section 10

a The groom is (afraid) of the dog.

b The groom tells the Count to 'mind' the dog because 'he flies at everybody'.

> A character's speech can often suggest their feelings.

7   PB1 Section 10

a Count Fosco is (not even slightly afraid) of the dog.

b He puts his hand on the dog's head and looks him 'straight in the eyes'.

> The writer's choice of words to describe a character's actions can often suggest their feelings.

8   PB2 Section 11

'he flies at everybody!'

9   PB2 Section 10

Talking to him disrespectfully

> Look for clues in the context that surround the word or phrase you are asked about.

10   PB2 Section 11

a false

b you daren't so much as look me in the face

> Look for evidence in the text that agrees or disagrees with the statement in the question.

11 PB2 Section 13

It gives emphasis to the Count's description, making him sound annoyed with the dog.

> Alliteration is often used to add emphasis to an idea or description.

12 PB2 Section 12

The word 'brute' suggests the dog is vicious.

13 PB2 Section 10

  a The dog is no longer fierce.

  b 'the dog crept back meekly to his kennel'

14 PB2 Section 12

Example: I think the Count is brave because he shows no fear of the vicious dog. I also think he is vain because he is annoyed that he has got the dog's slobber on his waistcoat.

> Remember to state your opinion then explain why you think that.

15 PB1 Section 11

Example: The Count faces a vicious dog quite calmly by showing it no fear. The dog is quickly tamed and goes back quietly to its kennel.

> The summary focuses on only the most important ideas in the text.

Spelling, punctuation and grammar

16 PB2 Section 6

'Are we lost,' asked Mum, 'I'm sure we've been past that house three times now.'

> There should be a question mark after 'Are we lost'. The next piece of speech is a new sentence, so there should be a full stop after 'asked Mum'.

17 PB2 Section 5

I couldn't understand why the television wouldn't work.

> In both cases, the apostrophes are positioned between **n** and **t** because **o** has been missed out.

18 PB2 Section 1

Example: Thomas, who was only six years old, wanted to be an astronaut.

> You could also use brackets to separate the parenthesis, or place it in a different place. For example: Thomas wanted to be an astronaut (he was only six years old).

19 PB2 Section 4

The river got higher and: it looked like it was going to overflow.

> It should be 'The river got higher; it looked like it was going to overflow' or 'The river got higher and it looked like it was going to overflow.'

20 PB1 Section 3

I only ate one slice of pizza, some cucumber and none of the garlic bread.

> In the first sentence, the comma should be after 'drink'. The second sentence needs question mark. The third sentence is a list, so the first and second items should be separated with a comma.

21 PB2 Section 5

She'd never believed she could beat Iris's record.

22 PB2 Section 4

To keep safe on your bike: always look where you are going, even if you're with an adult; be aware of other traffic around you, especially at junctions; and always wear a helmet.

> Use a colon to introduce a list. Count the number of items in the list, including any information used to describe them, and use a semi-colon to separate each one.

23 PB1 Section 4

a <u>Although he is a famous historical figure</u>, very little is known about him.

b He was greatly respected <u>because he was so honest</u>.

c <u>When she finished</u>, the audience gave her a standing ovation.

> Subordinate clauses begin with a subordinating conjunction showing how the subordinate clause links to the main clause.

24 PB2 Section 7

We took (two) cakes (to) Aunt Glenda and Uncle Barry's party. There was far (too) much food and we ended up bringing one home again.

> 'Two' is a number. 'To' is a preposition of direction. 'Too' means an excess of something, or 'in addition'.

25 PB1 Section 1

Saturn is a <u>much larger</u> planet than Earth but it has a <u>much shorter</u> day.

> An adjectival phrase is a group of words that give more information about a noun. In this sentence, the adjectival phrases give information about the nouns 'planet' and 'day'.

26 PB1 Section 2 Example: Every week, I **go** to drama club. Soon, we **will begin** rehearsals for a show called *Oliver*. It **is** a musical about an orphan.

> The adverbials 'Every week' and 'soon' give clues to the appropriate tense.

27 PB2 Section 3 She trained very hard but, sadly, did not win a medal.

> Examples of coordinating conjunctions include 'and', 'but', 'or' and 'so'.

28 PB2 Section 6 'I have come to see you,' said the mysterious stranger, 'because I have something to tell you.'

> Look out for sentences of direct speech that continue after phrases such as 'he said' or 'she said'.

29 PB2 Section 2

a at   **b** time

> In this sentence, the preposition indicates the when something happened, so is a preposition of time.

30 PB1 Section 1

noun phrase

> Each word in this group of words adds information to the noun 'night'.

31 PB2 Section 3

I love my cat **although** I am not sure she loves me.

> Read the sentence aloud with the different options and consider which one makes the most sense.

32 PB1 Section 4

The passive voice is not used correctly.

> The form of the passive verb in this sentence should be 'was broken'.

33 PB1 Section 2

Hopefully I will have passed the eleven plus exam.

> The future perfect is expressed using 'will', 'shall', or 'going to' plus 'have'.

34 PB1 Section 6

a (ourselves) **b** (replies) **c** (crashes)

'Ourself' ends in **f**, so the plural is formed using the suffix **-ves**.
Reply' ends in **y**, so the plural is formed using the suffix **-ies**.
'Crash' ends in **sh**, so the plural is formed using **-es**.

35 PB1 Section 3

I played football on Tuesday, rugby on Wednesday and basketball on Friday so I was exhausted.

Check for capital letters, commas in lists and a punctuation mark at the end of the sentence.

36 PB2 Section 9

ni**e**ce

When the sound is /ee/, use **i** before **e** except after **c**.

37 PB1 Section 5

a The film was **dis**appoint**ing** because the story was so **un**believ**able**.

b My dog's behaviour is completely **un**predict**able** which makes him **im**poss**ible** to train.

38 PB1 Section 7

a The **government** makes decisions about the way our country is run.

b Sometimes I use a pen to **write** and sometimes I use a pencil.

c The **sign** on the door said 'Push'.

39 PB2 Section 8

Example: I **dusted**, **mopped** and **scrubbed** until the kitchen was spotlessly clean.

Because 'mop' and 'scrub' have one syllable and end in a consonant-vowel-consonant pattern, you double the final letter before you add the suffix. 'Dust' does not follow this pattern and so the final letter is not doubled.

40 PB1 Section 6

(4)

'Life' ends in **fe**, so the plural is formed using the suffix **-ves**.

41 PB2 Section 9

brought

Make sure you know the difference between 'bought' (the past tense of 'to buy') and 'brought' (the past tense of 'to bring').

42 PB2 Section 8

final**ly**

43 PB2 Section 7

Example: There were a lot of empty spaces in the cinema. Astronauts go into space.

'Space' can mean 'an area that is available or unoccupied', or it can refer to the universe beyond planet Earth.

Published by Pearson Education Limited, 80 Strand, London, WC2R 0RL.

www.pearsonschools.co.uk

Text © Pearson Education Limited 2018
Edited, typeset and produced by Elektra Media Ltd
Original illustrations © Pearson Education Limited
Cover design by Lukas Bischoff

The right of David Grant to be identified as author of this work has been asserted by him in accordance with the Copyright, Designs and Patents Act 1988.

First published 2018

British Library Cataloguing in Publication Data
A catalogue record for this book is available from the British Library

ISBN: 978 1 292 24667 3

Acknowledgements

We would like to thank Helen Lewis and Steph Niland for their invaluable help in the development and trialling of this publication.

Note from the publisher
Pearson has robust editorial processes, including answer and fact checks, to ensure the accuracy of the content in this publication, and every effort is made to ensure this publication is free of errors. We are, however, only human, and occasionally errors do occur. Pearson is not liable for any misunderstandings that arise as a result of errors in this publication, but it is our priority to ensure that the content is accurate. If you spot an error, please do contact us at resourcescorrections@pearson.com so we can make sure it is corrected.